The Romance of Weights and Measures

Also by Keith Gordon Irwin

THE ROMANCE OF CHEMISTRY:
FROM ANCIENT ALCHEMY TO NUCLEAR FISSION

THE ROMANCE OF WRITING: FROM EGYPTIAN HIEROGLYPHICS
TO MODERN LETTERS, NUMBERS, AND SIGNS

KEITH GORDON IRWIN

The Romance
of Weights and Measures

ILLUSTRATED BY JOHANNES TROYER

New York

THE VIKING PRESS

Contents

List of Illustrations   7

Foreword   9

How Engla-Land Became England: AN INTRO-
DUCTION TO THE STORY OF ENGLISH WEIGHTS AND
MEASURES   13

I. The Simple System of Measurement of Early
    England   21
    *The Measuring of Length and Distance · Fur-
    longs and Acres · The English Community
    Measures for Grains and Liquids · Home Life
    in Early England · The Rod of the Builder · The
    Plan for Weights*

    A Beginning for the Measurement Story: THE
    RECORD OF ANCIENT TIMES   46

II. In the Days of the Pyramids: The Story of
    Egyptian Measurement   47
    *Under Egyptian Sands · Exploits of a Big Man ·
    "He Who Dwells in the Great House" · Traders
    of the Sea · Measurement Units of the Phoeni-
    cians · The Egyptian Balance · Relation Be-
    tween the Phoenician Weights and Measures and
    Those of Early England*

5

III.   With Accent on the Foot: the Greek Story   81

Mahis and Thumb-breadths · Getting the Foot In · Solon and the Big Foot · The Romans Do Some Compromising

Effects of the Fall of Rome: AN INTERLUDE IN THE STORY OF WEIGHTS AND MEASURES   93

IV.   The Rebuilt Measures of England   96

The King's Rod · Londinium and the New London · Aver-de-peis · The Pint of London · The Ounce-of-Troyes

The Opening of a New World: AN INVITATION TO MENTAL ADVENTURING   112

V.   Some Adventures in Measurement   114

Gunter and the Acre · Old Miles and New · An Adventure in Coinage · A New French Plan for Weights and Measures · Spread of the Metric System · The Metric System in the United States

VI.   Nineteenth-Century Changes in English Units   128

That Bushel of Ours · Drams, Scruples, and Pharmacopoeias

Measurement Trends of the Twentieth Century: A PROGRESS REPORT   133

VII.   Trends in Measurement Practices   134

Mikes for the Mechanic · Self-registering Scales · Experiments in Avoiding Fractions · In Retrospect

Index   141

List of Illustrations

The migrations to England from the fifth to the eighth century A.D.   19

The armstretch   24

Acre-measurement with a chain   26

The Anglo-Saxon wand   31

Anglo-Saxon woman using the wand and tun   33

The builder's rod   39

The Danish *skale*   42

The coming of Menes to the Nile Valley   55

The lord's column and the king's column   59

The main centers of trade in the ancient Mediterranean world   66

Egyptian container measure   70

Three sizes of balance used in Egypt   72

Coins of the ancient world   76

Greek soldier stepping off a *bema* step   86

Solon   88

The "king's rod"   97

A fourteenth-century London merchant using avoirdupois weight units   104

Gunter's chain for surveying   117

The inch scale and the E-scale   137

The acre counter   139

Foreword

As a youngster attending country school, I asked my father about the size of an acre. He said he did not know *why* it was so, but an acre was a strip of land 4 rods wide and 40 rods long, and so could be figured as 160 square rods. The school arithmetic text defined the acre as an area 22 yards wide and 220 yards long, or 4840 square yards. My teacher insisted that the easiest way to find the number of acres in a field was to multiply the width of the land in feet by the length of the land in feet and to divide the product by 43,560. But her way did not seem at all easy to me. Even measuring the size of the school yard in feet, using a foot rule, was a terrible job. By that time I had decided that the acre was something that was not intended to be simple enough for a boy to understand.

Years later I came across a brief statement about the acre made by Flinders Petrie, the noted English scholar. He reported that he had measured ancient English buildings, studied old English laws, and read comments in old itineraries and in old church and monastery records. He had reached the conclusion that the measuring system for distances and farm lands in use in early England was ex-

9

tremely simple. He stated that the size of the acre, which was part of the old system, had been laid out in a very simple way, and he went on to describe it.

He made two other equally surprising statements. One was that early England had a measuring stick that matched the meter. It had almost exactly the same length and was divided into tenths and hundredths in the same manner. His other comment was that the foot length was not known in early days in England and the introduction of this length unit upset the entire measuring system and destroyed its simplicity. Both ideas were startlingly new to me. Could Petrie be right? I tried to find out more from his writings, but he had joined an archaeological expedition to excavate the ruins of an Egyptian city that had been buried under the drifting sands. Fascinated by his discoveries of the measuring methods of ancient Egypt, he was too busy to bother with English records. In fact he never filled out the part of the English story that related to the measures for the harvest and for weights.

For a number of years I have gone ahead with the exploration of the English records, tracking down the reports of archaeologists, historians, and other scholars. Here, in these pages, is the elaborated story—begun by Flinders Petrie—of how the English weights and measures came to be.

The Romance of Weights and Measures

How Engla-Land Became England

AN INTRODUCTION TO THE STORY OF ENGLISH WEIGHTS
AND MEASURES

To get our story of weights and measures under way we shall be visiting England. But it is the land of fifteen centuries ago that we want, not the land of today. The Jutes will already have arrived to take over the land to the north of the white cliffs of Dover. The Angles will soon be coming across the North Sea in large numbers. Saxon war-boats will be darting in and out of the river mouths along the southern shores of England. For this great island across from France one era of history is closing, another is about to begin.

As the story opens the country formed a part of the old Roman Empire. The Romans had called it the Province of Britain. A defending wall had been thrown along the northern boundary of the province to keep out land invaders. Defending fortresses had been built along the eastern and southern shores to repel invaders who might come by sea. Paved military roads connected into a single network the ways, often cut through forests, by which the trained soldiers of the Roman legions could be moved swiftly from point to point. With these walls, fortresses, and legions the Romans were well able to hold and defend Britain.

The Roman people, used to sunny Italy, did not like the climate of this northern province. It was chilly in winter, cloudy in summer. It rained too much. So the only people from more pleasant places who came to Britain to live were the soldiers, the military officials, and some merchants and traders. Only a small portion of this defended province was really occupied by the Romans. The military posts were on the military highways, and the highways had been built only for strategic purposes. Away from the highways there were large areas with deep forests. There were also treeless areas with almost barren hills, while along the rivers running through the interior of the country the dampness from abundant rains made pastures that were deep with grass. Regions like these— forests, barren hills, deep pastures—did not make good grain farms. There were, it is true, some sections of the province where grain could be grown. The Roman officials made their homes in such places; their crops were cared for by military slaves. One of these sections was the south side of the Thames River, across from the military post of Londinium (London). The valley of York in more northern Britain was even better for grain farming; here was the military capital of the province. The Britons, who were the natives of the land, kept largely to the lush pasture lands where there was an abundance of feed for their cattle and pigs. Their simple homes were apt to be located in clustered groups along the dells.

After several centuries of widespread military control, the great Roman Empire collapsed. Its military power had been wasted as army generals fought among themselves to become the next emperor of Rome. In this fighting, whole legions were destroyed. Toward the last, even Rome itself needed to be protected. Legions were withdrawn from the various outlying Roman provinces to protect the city. In the case of Britain, only a few legions had been left to defend the province. In the year 407 the last two legions in Britain received orders to embark on boats for the Continent. The people of Britain were assured that these legions were being borrowed for emergency duty and would soon be returned. Three years passed. The military posts were, of course, without soldiers to man them. Stores that had catered to military trade were boarded up. In the larger population centers the people wrote pleading letters to the emperor, begging him to let the legions come back to defend them.

In 410 they received their reply. The emperor was sorry, but there were no legions for Britain. Rome could no longer defend this part of its Empire. The welfare and protection of the land was left to the people themselves. The emperor wished them success. These people who had never been permitted to carry weapons and who had never been given any training in military self-defense were suddenly told they must defend themselves against invading foes. In a state of panic those who could do so crowded the piers of Londinium, seeking passage to France. Yet there were several cities, clustered around military locations, that kept on with their activities, partially manning the fortresses.

At Londinium, however, the warehouses were empty, the shops closed, the harbor deserted except for some fishing boats. The long wooden bridge spanning the Thames had only an occasional traveler crossing its unguarded length.

In the confused period that followed the withdrawal of the final Roman legions from Britain, several tribal groups from across the North Sea got a foothold along the island's shores. Historians think it probable that a rather mild change of climate occurred at this time, so that northwestern Europe got less rain than formerly. In any case, a decrease in the annual rainfall of Britain encouraged grain farming in many new areas. The Jutes from Sweden reached the island first, but they were few in number. Then came the Angles, in a migration that lasted for a century and a quarter. By the end of that migration period their entire tribe had reached the new lands across the North Sea. In time, Saxons from along the Elbe River, sailing across the same sea westward, attacked the southern shores of Britain. They had set out as marauders and plunderers but later established settlements.

In their migration the Angles took over the eastern part of Britain. A boat loaded with stout fighting men would appear off the coast of Britain. After rowing up some stream the invaders would make a sudden sortie.

If strongly opposed, the group would withdraw to strike again at some less protected spot. Eventually they would secure a strong foothold. Then the boat would be sent back for the wives, children, and family possessions. The first group of invaders would not advance far from the shore, but would build homes and lay out farms there. A little later another wave of newcomers might land at the mouth of the same stream. They would push past the first group and build their homes farther upstream. So, gradually, the country went on filling up with people from across the North Sea. The native peoples who had been living in these districts were to move toward the higher hills, stubbornly and slowly, taking their possessions with them.

The Saxons who struck along the southern shores of Britain formed but a part of the entire Saxon confederacy of tribes that had occupied sections of Germany. Unlike the Angles, these Saxons, intent on plunder, went to the places where the possibilities of plunder and pillage would be greatest. They appeared off the mouths of large streams and operated as huge war parties, ready to ravish the settlements near the shore. The old Roman fortresses, now only partially defended because there were so few trained men, offered some resistance to the marauders. But the defenders were taken and destroyed. After that, the Saxons moved quite readily inward from the seacoast. The fortified Roman military posts spaced out along the military highways were destroyed completely. The native Britons were forced back to Cornwall and the fastnesses of Wales. By this time, the Saxons had decided to settle in the conquered land and had sent for their families and possessions. Eventually the paths of the Saxons, as they moved from the southern shores of Britain northward toward the central part of the country, reached the paths of the westward-moving Angles. But this situation did not produce a conflict between the tribal groups, for the two peoples spoke essentially the same language and had the same customs.

Back across the North Sea there had been an old Engleland. That land was now deserted. Westward of that sea was a new Engle-land—or Engla-land, as they referred to it. The language spoken there is known today as Anglo-Saxon, meaning Engla-Saxon, but to the people of England it was Englisc. Because of the slowness and completeness of their invasion of the country, these peoples did not mingle with the Britons or Romans who had lived in the land before. There was no intermarriage with them, no blending of manners and customs. The farmland of the invaders had been measured according to a system familiar to the Angles and Saxons; again there was no blending of measurement units with those of either the Romans or the Britons.

There is another portion of the invasion story to be added. Just before the time of Alfred the Great, the famous king of the West Saxons, an invading group from northern Denmark and southern Scandinavia—whom history refers to as Danes—fought their way into the Angle country of north-central England. Moving south-

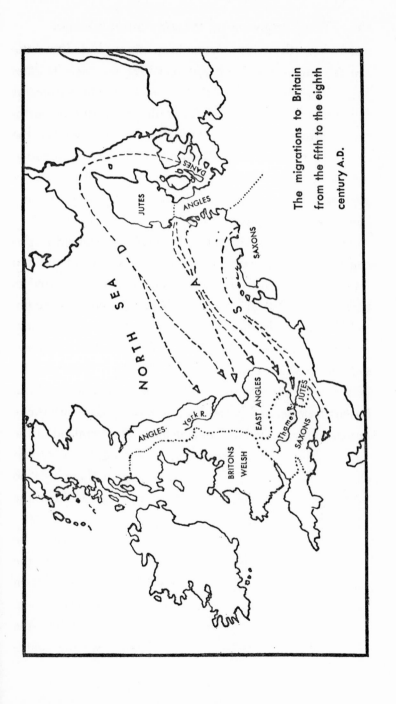

The migrations to Britain from the fifth to the eighth century A.D.

ward along the wider rivers, they struck deep into the country and settled in groups near the rivers. In customs and habits the Danes and Angles were much alike. Their farm measurement plans were identical. In language there were differences, but the variations were more largely in word forms than in the language structure.

In a century or so these newcomers, who had at first kept wholly to themselves, became completely assimilated. As their language became blended with that of the Angles, pairs of words might be kept, one of each pair coming from the speech of the Danes and the other from the speech of the Angles. As examples of such pairs that have lasted on, side by side, to become a part of today's English language, we have *nay* and *no*, *raise* and *rear*, *fro* and *from*, *screech* and *shriek*, *kirk* and *church*, *sick* and *ill*, *hide* and *skin*, *shank* and *leg*. To the Danes of England we are indebted for such words as *wife*, *husband*, *bride*, and *home*. For these the Angles had used *my woman*, *my man*, *my new woman*, *my house*.

I

The Simple System of Measurement of Early England

Alfred the Great, King of the West Saxons eleven centuries ago, became the first king of all England when his power was extended to take in the Angle and Danish areas. One of his acts, as a king, was to have standards constructed that would show the merchants of outside countries the true and exact size of English length units, English weight units, and English measures for liquids and grains. Copies of measuring rods, weight units, and grain measures, stamped officially, could be obtained by a merchant at low cost.

In 950, about a century after Alfred's birth, these standards of Alfred were transferred to London to be placed in a special room in Westminster Abbey. There, officials continued Alfred's plan of preparing and checking copies of these standards. Four centuries later, in the time of Edward III, some additional units were added to Alfred's list to take in new measures that had been introduced. In addition, the old standards were carefully duplicated, more permanent materials being used in the construction.

Alfred's standards did not include such present-day units as the foot, yard, pound, gallon, or bushel. Corresponding to them were units that are now obsolete. It would be easy, then, to suppose that many units of the weight and measure system brought to England by the Angles, Saxons, Danes, and Jutes were carelessly designed or crudely related to other units and that, later, others were introduced to improve the situation. But Flinders Petrie, who, as we have seen, made the first intensive study of the measurement system of early England, found that the system for distances and farm-land measurements had not been crude or illogical. Instead, it was one of the best that the world has ever known. It was with the units inserted later that the trouble began.

The most available source of information about these findings of Petrie is that given on pages 481, 482, and 484 of Volume 28 of the Eleventh Edition of the *Encyclopædia Britannica,* published in 1910. There, as a part of the lengthy article on "Weights and Measures" which is signed with his initials, Petrie makes such statements as these:

"The basis of the present English land measures . . . are neither Roman or Briton in origin.

"We can restore the old English system of long measures from the buildings, the statute-prohibitions, the surviving chain and furlong, and the old English mile shown by maps and itineraries."

The old plan proved to be decimal in nature, and Petrie likens it to the metric system of today:

"It is remarkable how near this early decimal system is the double of the modern decimal system.

"Unfortunately the old equivalent of the meter has now disappeared. . . . Had it not been unhappily driven out by the 12-inch foot we should need but a small change to place our measures in accord with the meter."

The Measuring of Length and Distance

The measuring plan of early England was built around the length of body parts. The basic unit of the plan was the distance that the Angles called the *armstretch* and that the Danes referred to as the *faedm* (fathom); it referred to the spread of the outstretched arms, counting from the tips of the middle fingers. Actually the human armstretch would vary somewhat in length from warrior to warrior but *the* armstretch, as an official measure, had a fixed size. Petrie checked its length and found it exactly the same in England as in Scandinavia, early Holland, and Germany. It had the length of 79.20 present-day inches! This great armstretch could have been the reach of some great warrior of the past—and probably was. It may have been close to the armreach of any of the chieftains of the Angles, Saxons, and Danes, or possibly to the reach of

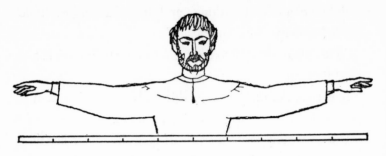

The armstretch

such other warriors as Charlemagne of the Franks and Richard the Lionhearted of England. In our own country men the size of Abraham Lincoln may have had arm-reaches somewhat like that.

As Petrie pointed out, the length plan of the great armstretch of 79.20 present-day inches was a decimal one. For smaller units it was divided into 10 and 100 equal parts. The smaller of these units was called a *fingerwidth,* since it was very nearly the width of the middle finger near its base. Ten fingerwidths matched the distance across the two hands pressed flat side by side. To the English people a "span" of oxen was a pair of them yoked together, so a *span-of-length* came to be used to represent the distance across the two hands—a space equal to 10 fingerwidths.

The units larger than the armstretch were also deci-mally arranged. Ten armstretches was a distance called a *chain.* Ten chains made a *furlong.* Ten furlongs made a *thus-hund.* The last word was their way of pronouncing "thousand" and the term was used to mean a thousand armstretches.

Put into table form, this is the plan for length and distance:

10 fingerwidths	= 1 span-of-length
10 spans	= 1 armstretch
10 armstretches	= 1 chain
10 chains	= 1 furlong
10 furlongs	= 1 thus-hund
(or 1000 armstretches)	

Since the armstretch of 79.20 present-day inches is close to twice the meter length of 39.37 inches, and both are parts of a decimal plan, it is easy to understand Petrie's comment, quoted on page 23, about the similarity of the two systems.

Furlongs and Acres

I have mentioned earlier how, as a boy attending country school, I had found the idea of the acre's size very perplexing and how the marking off of land into acres seemed a prodigious task. After reading Petrie's report on the measurement plan of early England, I realized that my ideas about the acre had been entirely wrong. I saw that laying out the land was very easy if one had the measuring tools of early England. All that was required was a light rope just 10 armstretches long with knots set an armstretch apart. This measuring rope was called a chain, perhaps because the arrangement of

Acre-measurement with a chain

knots seemed like a chain of beads. The distance it would mark off was a chainlength.

A 10-acre field was one that was just 10 chainlengths long and 10 chainlengths wide. Two people—one at each end of the chain—could lay out such a field quite readily. In early England such a block of land was always plowed from one end to the other. In that way the oxen would be turned around only at the end of the furrow—its furrow running the full length of the field. This meant that the field was a *furrow-long;* the English people shortened the term to *furlong.* So the furlong was of the same length as 10 chainlengths, or 100 armstretches; a 10-acre field was a *square furlong* in size. To change that field into ten fields of equal size the full length would be kept, the separate fields formed from strips a chainlength wide and 10 chainlengths long.

How simple the plan was! How simple the surveying!

The English Community

The handling of plowed land in blocks divided into ten equal strips was an important feature of English community life. Petrie does not elaborate upon this, for he was interested primarily in the measurements of the land rather than in the uses to which the land would be put. For details of agriculture and farm life in early England one must go to the records of English historians.

Of the tribal groups that invaded England soon after Roman times, the Angles made their settlements in the most methodical way. They came from across the North Sea in small sailing vessels, each vessel towing behind it a boat for the cattle and family possessions. For the main part of the migration, and perhaps for all of it, men came in groups of ten, with their families and possessions. Each group developed a settlement in which there were ten houses, each with its grounds for home, garden, and farmyard. In a favorable location, the plowland for the ten families was laid out as a 10-acre block, each family receiving a 1-acre strip. They drew lots for home locations and the acre locations, so that all might be treated alike.

This ten-family settlement was called a *thorp* or *town.*

The outer boundaries of the settlement were marked off from those of neighboring settlements by piles of stone or by lines of fencelike stakes that ran from one landmark to another. Usually the settlement was made where meadow-land gently sloping toward a stream could be cleared of bushes and shrubs and turned into plowland. The houses were placed on the somewhat higher ground away from the stream, each in its own fenced-in *croft* or *farmstead*. In the enclosure, the herb garden was placed near the house. It furnished savory seeds and spicy leaves for the cooking. The garden also included certain plants having a medicinal value, as well as plants giving colors for dyeing.

Beyond the herb garden was the farmyard. In it were such shedlike buildings as the "grain-place," which we call a *granary*, used for storing wheat and rye, and a special one for the barley that they spoke of as the *bar-ern* (barley-place) and we write as "barn." There was also a shed for the handling of milk and butter. At the rear of the enclosure was a stall constructed for a pair of oxen.

Between the plowed ground and the ten farmsteads was the grassy pasture land reserved for the smaller animals—calves, sheep, and lambs. Out beyond the farmstead area was the larger and, frequently, rougher pasture called the *commons*, where the larger animals were kept. It extended to the woodlands or outer boundaries of the settlement. From the woodlands the men cut firewood and logs for their building needs.

Though all the Angle settlements seem to have been laid out according to the same general pattern, no two were ever exactly alike in appearance. Each location was adapted to the contour of its own hills and the curves of its own stream. We may suppose, also, that the richness of the plowland was not identical in all areas of England, giving some variation in crop yields. But it can be stated with certainty that farming practices were good and that one acre of plowed land was sufficient for the needs of a family. It could furnish the wheat, rye, barley, and peas for the table, as well as the flax needed for weaving into linen. And there was another side to the matter. An acre was all the land that a family could handle at harvest time, since harvesting was a hand job. Several stalks of the mature grain would be caught by the hand, then cut by a stroke of the sickle. Other handfuls added to the first could form a bundle when tied with some twisted stalks. The bundles, stacked somewhat loosely, were then left until the grains matured thoroughly and the kernels could be shaken readily from the hulls. The bundles were next taken to the threshing floor, the bindings loosened, and the stalks flailed or trodden upon until the loosened kernels fell down into the chaff. The straw would now be raked away leaving the chaff and the kernels upon the threshing floor. On a windy day the material from the floor would be tossed into the air to let the wind blow the light chaff away. This last process was called "winnowing," which was a shortened word form for "wind-blowing." As the final step of the harvest the products were measured and stored.

Measures for Grains and Liquids

As was mentioned earlier, the standards of the time of Alfred the Great did not match those of today in relation to such measuring units as the quart, gallon, bushel, foot, and yard. The housewife of early England had measures that were far more simple than ours, however, and a measurement system for liquids and grains vastly superior to the one used in the United States at the present time.

In the English home of a thousand years ago, the products of the harvest had to be measured carefully. There would be no further supply for a whole year, so the problem of budgeting it was a very real one for the housewife. As the months passed, she would need to know how the supplies were lasting. Knowing that, she could decide, for example, whether to make a cake or use her wheat flour only for rolls. To us, who can go to the grocery if our flour bin becomes empty, it is hard to understand what a problem it was to keep an almost continual inventory of what was on hand. Without putting down on paper a single numerical figure, the housewife could take her measuring stick and in a moment report how many more loaves of bread she could bake with the rye flour left in a bin. Stepping into the house where the homemade ale was produced from barley and malt, according to a recipe that might have been centuries old, she could thrust her measuring stick down into the partially emptied vat and tell, almost instantly, how many days the ale in that vat would last.

It seems almost uncanny to us, today, that she could make these measurements so easily. But it is all explained by her measuring stick, which Petrie called "the old equivalent of the meter." It was just half as long as the old armstretch. Its length, then, was 39.60 present-day inches; the meter's length is 39.37 inches. It was divided decimally; so is the meter. It was used, as will be seen, to develop in a decimal way the container sizes for liquids and grains; so was the meter. The Angle housewife called her stick a *wand*. We might not think of it as a measuring stick at all were we to pick it up, since it carried no numbers. It was made from a smooth, round piece of slim white wood, and its length was divided into ten *handbreadths*, shown only by shallow but clear cuts made sideways across the wood. The handbreadth, in turn, was divided into ten parts, each called a *half-fingerwidth*, shown only by simple indentations in the wood. When used to measure some distance such as a table top, the counting of the handbreadths and half-fingerwidths could start at either end.

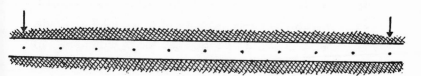

The Anglo-Saxon wand; distance between arrows is a handbreadth or 3.96 inches

The appearance of a portion of such a wand is suggested in the accompanying full-size drawing. On it the handbreadth distance would be 3.96 present-day inches. It may be that *your* actual handbreadth—counting across the knuckles of the hand and taking in the four fingers and the thumb as placed side by side—will match closely the one of the stick. If so, half your fingerwidth—counted across the base of the middle finger—will match the old half-fingerwidth. As pointed out by Petrie, the old handbreadth corresponds to the metric decimeter, the old half-fingerwidth to the metric centimeter.

The entire container plan of early England was built about the wand and its decimal divisions. The result was a simple system, decimal in nature, as easy as counting itself. The main small unit corresponded to the liter of the metric arrangement of today. The unit 1000 times as large corresponded to the metric *stere,* a cubic meter. The first of these could be used either for liquids or for grains and flour, the second for a liquid, such as ale.

In the Angle kitchen the measure was a common object. Made of light wood in box form, open at the top, its inside measurements had a width, length, and depth of 1 handbreadth each. Its capacity of a cubic handbreadth was called a *measure-full.* Recipes for breadmaking appear to have always used flour by the measure-full. In the special shed where ale was kept the homemade liquid was prepared in one or two vats having spigots at the bottom for drawing off the ale. Made of heavy wood in boxlike form, the vat inside was a wand-length wide, a wand-length long, and a wand-length deep. The capacity of

Anglo-Saxon woman using the wand and tun

a cubic wand was a *tun*. The tun could also be counted as 1000 measure-fulls, as indicated from the vat's dimensions.

In addition to these two basic units for container size, several others were in common use in the home. All were related to the measure-full in a simple way. For liquids the *tankard-full* was just half a measure-full. Four tankard-fulls was a *lippy;* two lippies made a *bowl-full.* For grains the *peck* had the capacity of eight measure-fulls, while 16 pecks was counted as a *hlot.* Incidentally, the word hlot soon changed to *lot.* When the women said that 16 pecks was a *lot* of peas they may often have meant a LOT of peas.

The bins used for the storage of grains and peas always had inside measurements in handbreadths. One holding a peck would be 2 handbreadths wide, long, and deep, while half a hlot would be held by a bin 4 handbreadths wide, long, and deep. If the housewife had half a hlot of peas, she could serve peas porridge on Sundays and Woden's-days (Wednesdays), using a measure-full of the dry peas each time, and have just enough for eight months. To have enough for a whole year she would have had to start the year with an additional fourth-hlot of stored peas if she served the porridge twice a week. Her reasoning was simple. A peck of such peas would last four weeks, since the peck was equal to eight measure-fulls and she would be using two measure-fulls each week. The four weeks could be counted as a "monath" (month) and the year as twelve monaths. She would need 12 pecks, then, if she served peas twice a week. So, looking at the quantity of peas in the bin at harvest time, she would have made her plans for the year. It was long-range budgeting, but it was relatively simple and the method could be applied to the rye, wheat, and barley that went into similar bins.

The housewife who wanted to check on her ale supply that remained in a particular vat used her clean wand as a dip-stick, thrusting it to the bottom of the vat to see how far the liquid came up the stick. For every half-fingerwidth of liquid level she had 10 measure-fulls or 20 tankard-fulls of ale. If she used 5 tankard-fulls a day that amount would last four days. Such was the way the women of early England made the numerical problems of the home easy.

Home Life in Early England

Something should be said about the home life and the family activities of early England. Each settlement raised its own cattle and sheep, made its own garments, produced all its own food. Each family of the community did most of these things for itself.

The women milked the cows and made the butter and cheese. They sheared the sheep and combed the wool. They spun the wool and wove it into cloth for warm outer garments. They soaked the stalks of flax, beat the stalks to release the plant fibers, then made the fibers into threads that were woven into a coarse linen for clothing worn next to the body. It was the men who ground the wheat and barley into flour, grinding it coarsely to make grits or more finely for wheat meal. It was the women who did the baking. Much of the ground grain went into common rolls. There would also be loaves of white bread made from wheat meal and, occasionally, raised bread or cake. As another task the women tended the bees and stored the honey and wax. It was they who looked after the ale and supervised the soap-making and the dyeing of cloth.

It fell to the men to do the outdoor work associated with the plowing and planting of crops. At harvest time the entire family would be busy, but the heaviest work was done by the men. The men also did the butchering and the cutting of firewood. At off-season times they fished in the stream and set traps for wild game, and in winter the men of the community took turns in looking after the herds and flocks in the pastures, being particularly alert through the long nights when wolves came hunting through the forests. They were also the "Minute Men" of their day, trained for almost instant response in defense of their community and their homes.

The farm home of that day would appear to us to have no conveniences and only a small measure of comfort. The idea of the chimney as a way of carrying off the smoke of a fireplace had not as yet reached England in the days of Alfred the Great. In the homes of that time the smoke from the fire of hearth or oven passed out through holes in the roof. Our word "window" was originally *wind-hole,* or place of ventilation. The windows of early England had no glass, and the openings were covered at night and in bad weather by heavy shutters. The furniture of the home was simple. The food table was made of light-weight planks set on movable trestles; the planks were placed against the wall when not in use. The father and older boys made a bedroom of the dining room at night, sleeping on pallets of straw on the earth floor with two or three sheepskins for cover. The women and children had a separate room and some meager comforts.

But life in early England was not cruelly hard. Devastating floods and withering drought were normally absent. The soil would grow crops that reached maturity before the frosts of fall. The men and women were rugged and well nourished, the children ruddy-cheeked and noisily

happy at work or play. If their story makes one think of
that of the pioneers who advanced the frontiers of America, it is quite right that it should. But the men of early
England had no guns, since gunpowder had not yet been
invented.

The Rod of the Builder

The men of early England were outstandingly skilled
in all phases of woodworking. There were then no saw-
mills, planing mills, or woodworking shops. Each community developed its own carpenters, its own craftsmen,
its own boatbuilders, even its own wheelmakers. Almost
everyone among the men of the place could cut a tree in
the forest, hew it into a squared timber with smooth flat
sides, then split the timber into straight finished-lumber
planks or boards, to be used in building. To construct a boat
required the combined skills of many men and the guid-
ance of a master boatbuilder; if the boat was large and
intended for long voyages, the men of several communities would combine their efforts.

Metal tools were needed for this woodworking. The
two-bladed ax was important. The adz, with its flattened
blade set at right angles to the handle, was necessary for
the preparation of flat surfaces on planks or boards. The
bronze saw, with its coarse teeth, was used for squaring
up the ends of timbers and planks. Metal wedges were
for splitting the timbers into planks or boards. Bronze
chisels were used in cutting the slotted parts of wood

pieces that fitted together. The metal wedges and chisels had to be pounded with a maul or hammer.

As a carpenter's measure for lengths the men of early England used a combined rule and level. This tool, made of straight-grained wood, had a length exactly equal to five wand-lengths. The base was perfectly smooth and even, the sides were squared with the base, and along the top surface ran a shallow groove. The groove was deepest at the exact midpoint of the length, becoming slightly less deep on either side. Water would be poured into the groove when the device was to be used as a level. If the first drops remained at the very center and did not move to either side the tool was exactly level. Even a very slight lowering of one end of the tool would move the water toward the lower end.

This hand-produced tool was known merely as a *rod* or *pole*. Like the wand, it carried no numbers, the divisions being shown by vertical marks cut on the sides. Deep but sharp cuts divided the rod's length into 10 *ells*. The term "ell" was the old word for arm; we still use "elbow" (ell-bow) as the name for the bending point of the arm. The ell, in this case, meant the forearm, as it represented the distance from elbow to finger tip. As you can see for yourself, the forearm distance is just a fourth of the reach of the outstretched arms. Spread your arms wide; then, bending your arms at the elbows, see if your finger tips do not meet at the center of your mouth. More shallow cuts divided each ell on the rod into 20 *thumb-breadths*. The name "thumb-breadth" was used

The builder's rod

because the distance was close to the width of the thumb as measured just below the base of the nail.

The Danes called each of the deeper cuts on the rod, which marked the position of the ells, a *skaar*. The Angles called it a *skore*. The present English spelling is *score*. The timber men and boatbuilders of that time gave distances marked on pieces of wood as these distances would be counted on the rod. Thus a count of "three score and ten" meant a count of 3 heavy marks, for ells, and 10 light marks, for the additional thumb-breadths. The total was 70 if given in thumb-breadths. In the Gettysburg Address, Abraham Lincoln used the lumberman's language but applied the counting to years rather than to lumber as he opened his address with the words, "Four score and seven years ago."

The rod as a carpenter's tool was in frequent use on the farms of early England. Timbers for the house were cut a rod long, walls were made half a rod high, the stall for the pair of oxen was a rod wide and a rod long, barnyard posts were set a rod apart. Planks were made 2 thumb-breadths thick, and boards were 1 thumb-breadth thick. Firewood was cut to a length of 2 ells and hearths were made 4 ells wide. For many of these measurements the man of early England who did his own carpentering used, instead of his awkwardly long measuring rod, a light cord that was just a rod in length. This cord, which had knots an ell apart, was convenient for use in the forest at the time of the cutting of timbers for sheds and other buildings. Also, with a weight hung at one end, a piece of the cord's length made a plumbline that could check on whether a wall was exactly vertical. Finally, it was useful in piling up wood for the home fires. A *cord* of wood meant a pile whose length, width, and height added together was just the cord's length.

The Plan for Weights

The final section of the system of measurement in use in early England relates to weight. I wish that I had known about this weight plan when I was a youngster in country school. I had been very concerned as to how anyone would know how heavy the pound ought to be if he had no pound to start with. I asked my older brothers about it; they did not know. I suggested that someone could have picked up a stone that seemed just right to *pound* with and said, "Let's call this weight a pound." They laughed at me and said that my idea was very foolish. But they had no better idea to offer.

The weight system of early England turned out to be

very simple. It has already been mentioned that a measure-full of peas or flour was an important quantity in the Angle kitchen and that the measure itself was a boxlike vessel that was just a handbreadth wide, long, and deep on the inside. *The heaviness of a measure-full of cool water gave the Angles their basic weight unit.* Cool water was chosen so that it would always have the same density. The matter was as simple as that! This unit was called the *measure-weight.*

The *tun-weight* was exactly 1000 times as large as the measure-weight. It was the heaviness of a cubic wand of cool spring water. Again, the matter was simple. The third unit of weight was the *skeat* (also spelled sceat), which was one-thousandth as heavy as the measure-weight. The word itself means "piece"; this small weight was used for the little silver coins minted by the early Saxon kings.

The most common weight unit of early England was not the measure-weight but one just half as heavy. Actually it represented the heaviness of a tankard-full of cool spring water. Usually this unit was called merely *the* weight or the *skale-weight.* Today it is sometimes referred to as the "early-pound," or "the pound of Alfred." Three other units were almost as common in their use as the skale-weight itself. The *hundredweight* was equal to 100 skale-weights. The *half-hundredweight* was half as large as the hundredweight. The *stone* or *stone-weight* was one-eighth of a hundredweight.

The weighing device that was used in the communities

The Danish *skale*

of early England was a unique type that is seldom seen today. Its Danish name was a *skale*. (We shall keep that spelling for the device, since the present spelling of "scale" or "scales" is now used for any weighing device, no matter what its form.) It had a beam with a counterpoise weight fastened solidly to one end, and a basket or hook hanging from the other end. The object to be weighed was placed in the basket or hung from the hook. No loose or movable weights were used with the device and the beam was not attached solidly to the support upon which it rested. When used in weighing, the beam was placed upon the upper edge of a wedge and the beam, being loose, would be moved until the point of balance was found. Sharp but shallow notches cut on the lower side of the beam were for skale-weight readings.

Apparently each English community had a public skale for weighings up to ten skale-weights. Far more important was the larger form, on which the bags of clipped wool and bales of sheepskins could be weighed. It seems probable that this large community skale had weight notches only for the half-hundredweight and the eighth-hundredweight.

To determine whether a bag being filled with clipped wool weighed an even eighth-hundredweight, the bag would be placed on the hook of the skale beam after the beam itself had been moved to the eighth-hundredweight notch. If the bag and its contents were too light, the counterpoise end of the beam would not rise. More clippings would then be pushed into the bag until the counterpoise did rise and the beam balanced. The same idea was used in making up a pack or bale of sheepskins that would weigh a half-hundredweight.

It should be noted that there was an exact value to the eighth-hundredweight and half-hundredweight throughout early England. Each community, of course, could have built its own weight standards from the idea that a tankard-weight of cool water was a skale-weight. But that, apparently, was not done. Instead, a new community borrowed the standards of an older community, copying the half-hundredweight standard in iron and using a handle by which the weight would be lifted. The eighth-hundredweight was copied in stone, notches being left in the stone for the fingers to use in lifting the weight. This second model was almost always called the *stone* or *stone-weight*. With these two standards available, the notches on the skale would be placed in correct positions.

To see why weighing was important in those days, we shall take a quick glance at the situation in England a thousand years ago. As already stated, the plowland of an Angle settlement was so divided that each of the ten families was to have an acre for its own crop use. But what happened as the settlement grew older? As the children of the first settlers grew to manhood and womanhood would there be any plowland for *them?* The historians give us the answer. The oldest son brought his wife to the home of his father and mother. He assisted his father with the farm work, looked after the land when his father became old, and inherited the land when his father died. A younger son was expected "to go out into the world to seek his fortune." In early England this meant that he would join a group of other young men, under an older leader, who would seek out a desirable location for a new settlement. Then they would send back for their young wives and their meager family possessions, the family traveling either by ox-drawn cart or by boats that skirted the English shore line. It was in this way that the Midlands of England were taken over by the adventurous younger sons of many generations; and, in time, it was the way that the Angle migrations extended northward into Northumbria, the "land north of the Humber River."

It was easier for these younger sons and their wives to become established in their new settlements than it had been for their ancestors to make the difficult passage of the North Sea in reaching the new Engla-land. But both the newer and the older groups must have had the perplexing task of getting together the necessary tools made of metal that each family had to have in its pioneering life. The man needed a two-bitted ax for all timber work; an adz for smoothing a plank's surface; a maul and wedges for splitting logs into planks and boards; a coarse-toothed bronze saw for squaring the ends of pieces of lumber; a sickle for the grain harvesting; a long-bladed knife for hunting and butchering and his own shaving; and iron parts for his plow and for his defensive armor. His wife needed metal shears for clipping the sheep and for other uses about the home; an iron kettle for soap-making and another for cooking; and knives for the kitchen. Today's housewife has many utensils of metal not included in the early lists. The woman of a thousand years ago made her thimble—which she called a *thumb-bell*, for it fitted over the thumb—out of horn; her needles were made from splinters of bone; her spoons and tank-ards were of wood; and she used sharpened sticks of hardwood instead of forks.

The Angles, like the Saxons, Jutes, and Danes, were not metal-miners and never had been. To get the necessary tools, or metal for them, the Saxons looted the Roman locations along the coast of Britain. The Angles got theirs by trade. What they could supply for the trade was surplus grain, unused bags of wool clippings, and bales of sheepskins, with or without wool. The wool clippings and the bales of skins would be handled by weight. The Angle communities became noted for the high quality of their products and the accuracy of their weighing. These were just as important then as they are today.

A Beginning for the
Measurement Story

The decimal plan for the units of weight and measure
as used in early England was so remarkably simple that
the English people would like to give themselves the
credit of inventing the plan. But the entire system had
been developed in ancient times along the shore lines
and caravan routes of the eastern Mediterranean world.
Before that, length units had in decimal divisions been
used to measure the sizes of the pyramids of Egypt and
to mark the rise and fall of the Nile water in floodtime
and between the time of seed-planting and the harvest.

II

In the Days of the Pyramids:
The Story of Egyptian
Measurement

In 1881, Flinders Petrie went to Egypt on an archaeological expedition. He was only twenty-eight at the time
but was already an outstanding authority in metrology,
the science of measurement. This particular expedition
was setting out to excavate the ruins of an ancient
Egyptian city that had long been deserted and was at
that time buried under drifting sands. Petrie went along
as the metrologist of the party. He measured the walls
and the dimensions of the temples and other structures
as they were uncovered. He wanted to find out the details
of any measurement plan then in use and the relation between the various units. Perhaps after this city had been
excavated, he might be able to reach a conclusion as to
the measurement plans that were in use when history
began.

Forty years went by. Petrie spent at least a few months

of every year among the ruins of ancient Egypt—digging
and measuring and studying. He kept in touch with those
who had been studying the story of early measurement as
shown in the ruins of other places of an ancient world.
In the Fourteenth Edition of the *Encyclopædia Britannica* he summed up the facts he had found about the
measures of the ancient world, giving this as a part of
the articles on weights and measures. In its enormous
amount of detail, the article is confusing. Yet certain points
stand out. The Egyptians invented the decimal plan for
measurement units and used it consistently. Other peoples
of the ancient world around the Mediterranean Sea based
their length plans upon that of the Egyptians and also kept
to the value of basic Egyptian units. But there is a third
conclusion, which Petrie only hints at: The plan of early
England for distance and farmlands had the same decimal
relationship of units as did that of ancient Egypt, but the
two plans were not based on the same size of the armstretch. In Egypt the armstretch was equal to 73.64
present-day inches, not 79.20 inches as in early England.

Under Egyptian Sands

Ancient Egyptian history has left its record of measurement as a readable story. Petrie found, cut into rock, a
scale of length units used in keeping track of the rise and
fall of the Nile waters at floodtime. This scale might have
been cut five thousand years ago. He found mural paint-
ings that show surveyors at work with a knotted cord

measuring out farmland. Under the sands that had drifted across the pillared portico of the Temple of Anubis in ancient Memphis on the west bank of the Nile he found a model cut from stone for the *apet,* a wheat measure of that long-ago time when there was a public market facing the temple. In the burial tomb of a high priest, who in life was "Sealer of Weights and Measures," were found the standards that he used in his official work.

Upon the rock-cut scale by the Nile there were no names or numbers. Petrie reported that the smallest divisions were for *zebos,* the word zebo meaning finger-width. Every tenth line was emphasized, this divisioning corresponding to the English span-of-length; Petrie calls it "the lesser span." The armstretch length of 100 zebos had the Egyptian name of *nent.* The length of the knotted rope used in land surveying was 10 nents or a *khet.* Two longer distances of the decimal plan applied only to distances along the river, 10 khets making a *cable-length* and 10 cable-lengths being a *thousand;* for the matching units the English had used the words furlong and thus-hund. Petrie states that he saw some of the old stone markers for thousands that indicated the distances along the river from Memphis.

Exploits of a Big Man

Memphis had been the capital of the country in the days of Khufu (or Cheops), the ruler who had the Great Pyramid built as his royal tomb. The city's location had been the headquarters of Menes, the first of the Pharaohs. Those stone markers along the river may have been set in place at the order of Menes. If so, the decimal measurement plan of ancient Egypt was developed either in the days of Menes or shortly before his time. Petrie does not venture a date for that development, but it must have been about fifty-five hundred years ago. There are reasons to believe that Menes himself took an interested part in the plan's production and application.

The life of Menes is vaguely legendary, for it came at a time when the hieroglyphic method of putting down words had not as yet been invented in Egypt. No tomb of his has been found, no palace of his has outlasted the centuries. Later artists pictured him as a big man, well-proportioned and strong. He was shown with a beard upon his chin and a tall helmet-like hat upon his head. It is evident, then, that he was an outsider, since Egyptian men were not tall and did not wear beards. (When Khufu became the first Pharaoh of his line, he put on a false chin beard when he appeared in public, used built-up soles on his shoes to make him appear taller, and wore a helmet-like hat as tall as the one of Menes, for he wanted to look like Menes.)

For many centuries before the coming of Menes, people had lived in the valley land of the Nile. They were not a primitive people but were alert, highly intelligent, inventive, and artistic. With such traits it is not strange that they were to build a type of life that was well adapted to the valley. The Nile was then, as now, a big river, whose waters flowed steadily through Egypt out into the Mediterranean Sea. It rises far to the south in the lofty mountains of central Africa, where an enormous amount of snow accumulates every season. The river, fed by melting snows, starts northward toward the Mediterranean, hundreds of miles away. Following a little rift in the earth's crust the mass of water flows majestically on, almost half-way across the continent. For much of the way it passes through a great expanse of unbroken desert. Near the southern boundary of what was to be the land of Egypt, the river enters a narrow valley. The steep rocky cliffs on either side had no trees, no bushes, no patches of grass. In the flat bottom of the valley—never more than a few miles wide—the only green color, before the coming of man to the valley, was that of scattered clumps of river reeds and papyrus plants whose roots were in the mud of shallow parts of the stream. As the river neared the sea it left the barren cliffs behind. Here, in what is known as the delta country, it divided into numerous smaller streams where the water moved sluggishly along passages half-choked with reeds. Among the marshes there were some patches of pasture grass and a few gnarled and stunted trees.

What a strange type of river the Nile might have seemed to an early man and woman looking from some cliffside out across the delta land and the desolate valley! Besides the green plants near the stream, the only living things they could see were flocks of birds that nested in the reeds or moved on long legs in the river mud. The river had some fish and a few hawks sailed the skies. What chance was there of making a home in a land like this?

The river had one peculiarity. In the heat of summer, great piles of snow on the high mountain plateaus of central Africa melt rapidly and send water cascading down the mountainsides. Floodwaters start down the Nile, and spread sideways beyond the banks, turning the river into a long, shallow lake. In time the floodwaters pass, the river returns to its banks, and the lands nearby, upon which a film of mud has been laid by the waters, begin to dry out in the summer sun. After that, the valley lies desert-dry until the floodwaters of another year.

Who first thought of planting wheat in the muddy fields just after the floods had passed? No one knows. Who selected a strain of wheat that would come to full maturity and produce a harvest in those days of the year between seed-planting time and the complete drying out of the land? No one knows. Who hit upon the idea of driving a herd of goats across the damp fields, to loosen up the ground and thus enable the land to hold its moisture longer as the wheat matured? That, too, no one knows. But the outcome is well known. The people of Egypt did grow wheat successfully along the river. They succeeded in growing a selected form of flax that could mature quickly, whose stems had a fiber that could be woven into fine linen. They found out how to grow such plants as garlic throughout the year by giving them water dipped from the river. They learned how to use dried leaves and stems from river plants as fuel for their fires and how to bake the clay found on the river banks into bowls, pots, and dishes. Because they had no wood with which to build boats they could not, at first, get from one side of the river to the other. Then they learned how to use the tough seven-foot seed stalks of papyrus plants, tied into bundles with river vines, as raftlike boats. After that they built traps for wild birds among the river reeds. By this time the life of the people had become so well adjusted to the peculiar features of the Nile valley that the years passed peacefully and smoothly. The population had increased slowly, the settlements spreading southward along the river banks.

The people along the Nile, undoubtedly thought that they were the only inhabitants of the earth, cut off as they were by desert, mountain cliffs, and sea from other peoples. Then, one day, a large boat came southward, moving against the current. It had a sail of linen cloth on a wooden mast and there were rowers to guide the boat and move it toward the shore. In the boat was a large man—a friendly man with a handsome beard. In the cool of the evening he stopped to talk with the people as they gathered along the shore. Legend implies that the settlements at that time reached southward only to the point where the valley narrowed sharply and at which an old channel branched off along a valley shelf on the south side of the river. This channel had apparently at one period carried a moderate supply of water, but at the time of which we speak it was dry except at floodtime. Then the water followed the old channel in a separate path toward the sea and did not return to the major channel. Most of it ran into a good-sized lake basin, and dried up after the floodwaters had passed.

The man with the beard was Menes. It can be supposed that he came from the north in a boat made of wood, and that he reached the Nile by pushing through a reed-choked river branch in the delta country. He had apparently become interested in the strange valley land and made a leisurely trip southward along the river. It was not at the time of the floods and no one was very busy in the simple farms along the shores. Menes must have checked thoroughly the old river channel that branched off on the south side of the river. He seems to have noted that if sand were removed from the channel, water would come through it at all times of the year. By the proper use of low banks of earth the oncoming water could be used to flood one set of fields, then released to flood other fields, and so on. The idea, known today as flood irrigation, is now in wide use in western America in getting river water upon land that would otherwise be too dry for crops.

There was another point for Menes to consider. If a small quantity of water would pass through the old channel throughout the entire year it could be led through ditches placed beside olive or fig trees or down a row of grapevines. Previously such a tree or vine, though valuable for its fruit, would die because of too much water

The coming of Menes to the Nile Valley

around the roots or wilt away when without water. But how was that old channel to be cleared out enough to let the water flow through it steadily? Menes, being a great organizer as well as an able thinker, solved the problem by getting the aid of the men of Egypt during the off-season of the year that came after the harvesting was over and before the new planting was begun. It seems that he offered them all the fresh bread and garlic they could eat, with some entertainment as well, if they would help with the project. The response was enthusiastic. To get ready for the work Menes had to start in a small way, probably taking several years to accumulate a supply of the needed foodstuffs and to get a large number of baskets made for removing the sand. But even as the water of the partially opened channel began to trickle, Menes seems to have been ready with his plans to make use of it in growing wheat, flax, olive trees, fig trees, and grapevines. The trees and vines were ordered from some outside country, since they had been previously unknown in Egypt. The new areas coming under cultivation belonged to Menes, and he used the crop returns from them in carrying out his ideas.

One idea of his had to do with a temple. We do not usually think of a temple as anything but a place devoted to religion, but Menes apparently felt that it should be a research center, a training school, and an industrial laboratory also. Near his own headquarters on the south side of the river, just where the delta country had its beginning and valley had its end, was a small temple. He supplied its priest with foodstuffs and linen for his workers and persuaded them to take up, in a practical way, some of the problems that needed attention. It may be assumed —and I think that the assumption is based upon fact— that Menes was particularly interested in having a practical system of measurement devised that could be used with the new irrigation projects. He wanted not only a form of unit that could readily be used in counting distances, but also a surveying arrangement for marking out the borders of the fields made by the low banks of earth.

From today's point of view, it can be seen quite readily why the measurement plan started with the fingerwidth and the distance across the two hands as shown by the span. This plan could be used for *counting*. In *number counting* the fingers of the hands were used, the thumb and fingers together. The two hands, then, gave a span of 10 fingers. For large numbers the hundred was counted as 10 spans, the thousand as 10 hundreds. The Egyptians used fingers and hands also to keep the same numbering simplicity for their measurement plan. The finger near its base was the beginning unit; the next unit, ten times as large, was the span of the two hands. For the third unit, ten times the span, they had the armstretch—that was as far as the body lengths would go decimally. For measuring fields and locating the positions of low banks of earth, a unit of ten armstretches was selected. For longer distances along the river the decimal plan was extended by two more units. But, simple as it was, for this plan to be highly useful for *all* Egypt, *one unit of the decimal series had to be given a fixed value;* then all units would have a fixed value, since they were decimally related to the main unit. This was done.

"He Who Dwells in the Great House"

History credits Menes with the establishment of a well-organized government in Egypt. The nature of that organization was quite distinctive. As the practice of dividing the fields with low banks of earth to catch floodwaters and use them more effectively was extended throughout Egypt, the necessary surveying was left in the hands of temple-trained workers. But disputes soon arose, and judges were needed. These men had to be familiar with the local situation and be able to make wise decisions. So Menes divided the country into *nomes*, placing each nome in charge of a lord or judge, whose decision in a local dispute would be final. In the case of disputes between two lords over some water right, the case went to Menes himself. He was *lord of lords* or *judge of judges*. His decision was completely final.

To give official importance to the position of each lord of the nome, Menes had these men live in homes that were larger than those of the common workers. In order that one lord might not consider himself of more importance than any other, the houses of all lords had to be of the same size. This appears to have been accomplished by requiring that all were to use a special building rule and make the heights and lengths of the houses the same number of unit distances on that rule. It is known that the basic unit on this builder's rule was the *mahi*, a term that meant forearm and so matched in idea the ell of early England. (Petrie usually calls the mahi by the Roman name of *cubit*, though that name did not come into use in Egypt until the days of Cleopatra.) The common houses of Egypt had roof beams and pillars made from bundles of the papyrus seed stalks bound with lotus vines. The houses of the lords followed the same building design but the main room was 10 mahis

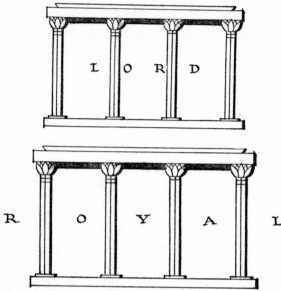

The difference in size of the lord's column, 10 common *mahi* high, and the king's column, 10 royal *mahi* high

in length and width, the pillars 10 mahis high and set half that far apart. Having no wood, the pillars were made from the same seed-stalk type of bundles as was used in the common house; elongated and enlarged in diameter by an overlapping of the individual stalks, they kept the same general appearance as that of the shorter pillars.

Since Menes was lord of lords he wanted a house larger than those of the lords. The matter of size was handled in a way that may seem odd to us. A royal mahi measuring rule was devised that represented the building units on an enlarged scale. Everything was made just twelve per cent larger than before, though why that particular proportion was selected may never be known with certainty. On the measuring rule the *royal zebo* was, then, twelve per cent larger than the common zebo, the *royal nent* was twelve per cent longer than the common nent. On the builder's knotted cord the *royal mahi* was twelve per cent longer than the common mahi—its length matching that of 28 common zebos, while the common mahi had been 25 common zebos.

It seems that Menes built the pillars for his house from the dried seed stalks, probably mixing in some cooked vegetable gums to give strength to the pillars. Later rulers had such pillars cut from hillside rock in a single piece, though they kept the seed-stalk appearance in the cut stone. Over a thousand years after Menes, all rulers of Egypt were called by the word "Pharaoh." This meant "he who dwells in the great house." Menes, then, could be counted as the first of the Pharaohs. As the power of the pharaohs extended to other lands they added to their title of lord of lords that of king of kings. Since they each wanted a house bigger than that of the kings under them, the lengths of the rock-cut pillars for their own "palaces" reached such enormous values and involved such great weights of stone that thousands of men were needed to move them from the rock quarries and get them raised into position.

Menes had the royal building units used for the temples of Egypt. This was to show that he and the gods were on a similar level of importance. That building policy was followed by later Pharaohs. As to the sizes of royal

tombs, Khufu put his grandiose ideas of his own importance into effect by having the Great Pyramid constructed as his royal tomb. It was seven *royal khets* high
and along each side of the square base it was eleven
royal khets wide. In terms of today's measures the height
was a bit over 481 feet, the length of each side just
756 feet.

Traders of the Sea

A few years ago a sealed room was discovered near
the base of the Great Pyramid. In it was a boat that had
been built for Khufu, for use in the life after death when
he would join the gods in passages across the skies. When
the covering slabs of rock were lifted from the boat a
faint odor of cedar wood was detected. Five thousand
years before, the cedar for that vessel had been cut on
the forested slopes of the Lebanon mountains at the
eastern end of the Mediterranean Sea. So had the spruce
and the fir used in the boat's parts. True, the long sea trip
from the hamlets at the base of the Lebanon mountains
to Memphis, the ancient capital city on the Nile, would
at that ancient time have been a perilous one. Only small
boats were then being built, and a small boat loaded with
logs of trees as cargo was then, as now, difficult to handle
in a rough sea.

As Egypt developed under the Pharaohs, wood was in
constant demand as a building material, and the trade
between the Lebanon country and the Nile, in which logs

of cedar, spruce, and fir were exchanged for baskets of wheat, cloth made of fine linen, rolls of papyrus writing material, or trinkets of ivory and gold, became quite important. By the year 1500 B.C. there was an established sea route from the port of Gebal along the Lebanon shore to Memphis, with a lumber fleet making the round-trip voyage each year. This port, whose name is mentioned several times in the Bible as a place of great shipbuilding activities and of able sea captains, does not appear under that name in any modern geography. The old harbor, once so busy, is now silted up; the fishing hamlet of Jubayl now occupies the little bay by the shore. In Greek and Roman times the city was called Byblos. The name Byblos was a Greek word meaning "City of Books" and probably came from its importance as a distributing place for Egyptian papyrus. The Greeks also named the strip of land at the base of the Lebanons, and the Romans were to use the Greek name. To these people, Greeks and Romans, it was Phoenicia and the people living there were Phoenicians. On today's maps the name of Lebanon has been restored; Jubayl is along the shore north of Beirut, the capital of the country.

Around 1500 B.C., a date mentioned previously, Gebal was a busy place. Its inhabitants were fishermen, shipbuilders, and workers in the timbered forests on the Lebanon slopes. The only outside customer for its logs of timbers was faraway Egypt. The boats in the port were varied in size and numerous, but none were really large by any standards of today. Each of those designed for longer journeys was built with a mast that could be taken out of its socket. These boats, like all other boats at that time, were drawn upon the beach at night; the masts would be taken down and the sail draped like a tent over the hull. In the morning the voyage would be renewed if the day was fair and the wind favorable.

A great discovery in the island of Cyprus, northwest of Gebal, made a sudden change in the activities of the people of the port and eventually made the place one of international importance. The island is a hundred miles to the west of the eastern Mediterranean shore. Some seamen had been blown that hundred miles by a great storm and, after managing to land safely, had discovered rich mines of copper on the island. Eager to carry the news back to the mainland, they finally got their boat, carrying ore samples, to the area from which they had been blown by the storm. The news of the finding of copper soon reached Gebal. The boldest sea captains and the wisest shipbuilders felt that it would be possible to get to the island if strong boats were built that could handle such a heavy cargo as copper. The sailing would have to be done by night as well as by day, and the sailing would have to continue whether the weather was favorable or not. How long it took to design and build the ore-boats, how long it was before a small fleet of such boats set out from the mainland, sailing westward for the initial trip to the island, is not known. It must be supposed that the island was reached, that some ore was dug out and loaded into the boats, and that at least some of the boats got back to the mainland successfully. From the records of history it is known that a sea route was worked out and used in certain favorable times of the year and that the mainland terminus was the harbor of Ugarit, directly east of the island. In addition to being the only desirable harbor along that coast, it had conspicuous white cliffs at either side of the harbor entrance that could be seen by men out at sea.

By way of digression, it should be explained that the copper from Cyprus was very pure, like that used today in an electric cable. When a quantity of it is melted with one-tenth as much tin, an alloy is formed that is known as bronze. Bronze is a truly wonderful substance. It is not soft, as copper by itself is. It can be ground to an edge that is strong and sharp. It can be melted and poured into a mold, thus making possible the rapid production of tools with an unvarying pattern. For the ancient world that had, as yet, no knowledge of steel, the discovery of bronze-making was one of the outstanding events. With bronze tools such as the two-bitted ax, the adz, and the coarse-toothed saw, men for the first time could cut down large forest trees with ease, could form the logs of the trees quite readily into planks and boards. Boat-building was now to be developed on a larger scale, both for boats carrying heavier cargoes and for those using more extensive sea routes. To the city of Babylon, an ancient city on the Euphrates River, went the copper and tin gathered from Cyprus and other parts of the eastern Mediterranean world, there to be made into bronze implements—

for the workmen of that industrial city knew the secrets of bronze work. Outward from Babylon went the caravans loaded with bronze tools and implements.

About the year 1300 B.C., the city and port of Ugarit came to a sudden end. A Hittite army came marching out of the rough country to the north that is now a part of Asiatic Turkey and took military possession of the unprotected place. The Hittite general expected to become rich from the tribute he would demand from the metal handlers. His plan failed, for the Gebal sea captains bringing in their loads of copper to Ugarit refused to land the metal. Turning south, they followed the shore line to the ports of northern Phoenicia. The caravan travelers bringing the finished bronze goods of Babylon stopped before they reached Ugarit. Retracing a part of their journey, they ended it at a Phoenician port. After that the warehouses of the city port behind the white cliffs remained empty; business had gone elsewhere.

The sudden catastrophe that overtook Ugarit was the beginning of an exciting new commercial life for the port of Gebal. Previously its only outside customer was Egypt. Now, as a commercial city of major importance, it was a center of trade. Caravans reached it from Babylon and Nineveh; its own boats touched all ports along the eastern Mediterranean as well as Memphis on the Nile. The king of the city, who had been pleased to be in the paid employment of the Egyptian Pharaoh, was now adding to his income and prestige by being in the pay of eastern kings as well.

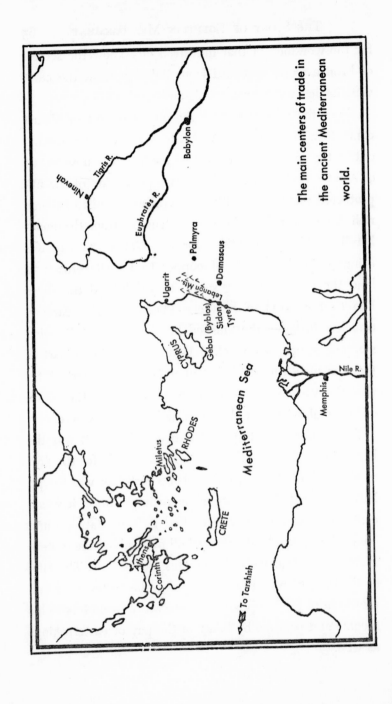

The main centers of trade in the ancient Mediterranean world.

The time of the great commercial expansion of Gebal may be placed at approximately 1200 B.C. The expansion was not due merely to the rerouting of trade through this city, however. The motions of the stars in the night sky were studied by the men of Gebal more fully than ever before, so that they might sail their boats at night with a knowledge of where they were going. A new manner of writing was developed, using an alphabet of letter sounds, by which messages could be written simply and readily. New industries were developed, old procedures changed.

By 1000 B.C., the two southern Phoenician ports of Tyre and Sidon had passed Gebal in the total amount of commercial activity. The initial reason for this was connected with the domestication of the Arabian camel. Since camels need water at less frequent times than the donkey or horse do, their caravan routes could be laid out more directly from Babylon to Egypt by leaving the Euphrates River at a point north of Babylon, then passing through the oasis city of Palmyra and on through Damascus, to stop on the Mediterranean coast near Tyre. The entire shore line of the Mediterranean Sea was now open to Phoenician trade and would flourish for centuries. Men in ships with bright-colored sails would be exchanging bronze tools and implements, fine linens—perhaps dyed with the wonderful "Tyrian purple" that gave the rich red reserved for royalty and high officials—or tiny glass vials filled with perfumes, in exchange for such things as animal skins, amber, and honey from wild bees. The alert Phoenician captains were trained to watch markings on the cliffs along the coast that would give evidence of metal ores. Copper ores were found and a tin ore discovered mixed with sand at the base of cliffs in Spain. But the most fabulous find of all was the rich deposit of silver probably in that southern part of inland Spain that was called Tarshish.

Measurement Units of the Phoenicians

In the centuries when Egypt was its sole outside customer, the city of Gebal, like other ports of Phoenicia, used the measuring plan of Egypt for lengths of timbers, sizes of fields, and distances along the sea. They used the mahi length for houses of officials and the royal mahi for the temple and the king's house. After the sudden commercial expansion of about 1200 B.C., some changes, apparently considered minor at the time, were made. The Egyptian nent (armstretch), divided into 10 and 100 parts, had been used up to this time in weaving linen and marking the dimensions of cloth. It was replaced in the Phoenician shops by a measuring rule just half as long, divided decimally into 10 and 100 parts just as the nent was, so that all corresponding measures were half as large. As a measuring device this new stick of the clothmaker was the equivalent of the wand of early England in all but unit size.

Around the *tefah*, or handbreadth, which was a tenth of the stick's length, a whole new plan of container sizes and weight units was developed, probably in Gebal. By the Phoenician traders the commercial use of such units was carried in a few centuries to all the lands around the Mediterranean Sea, and even beyond to all ports that the far-roving Phoenician sea captains visited.

The basic idea behind the new arrangement of units for container measures and units of weight is recorded by the scholar Melancthon W. Jacobus in *A Standard Bible Dictionary* (New York: Funk and Wagnalls, 1909, page 899):

"A unit of length would be selected, the cube of which gave the unit for measures of capacity; the weight of water contained in this cube gave the units for weights."

As a main unit of quantity, used for both liquids and grains, there was the *log*, just half a cubic handbreadth in size; it corresponded to the tankard-full of early England. The *chenica*, twice as large, was a cubic handbreadth in size; it corresponded to the measure-full of the English. For a weight unit, the heaviness of a log of water gave the *maneh* or *maneh-weight*. This corresponded to the skale-weight of early England. The heaviness of a chenica of water was, of course, two manehs. It was ordinarily given as 100 *shekels*, and each shekel was counted as 1000 *gerahs*; the little silver coin of early England that received the name of skeat corresponded to a tenth of a shekel.

Something needs to be said also about the Egyptian handling of container sizes and weight units, since the

Egyptian container measure

ways of the Egyptians—quite different from those of the
Phoenicians—had a marked influence on the measurement
systems of the ancient world. The Egyptian plan was built
about a counting scheme for kernels of wheat. A certain
small container was made just large enough to hold
1000 kernels of the grain. Experiments showed that it
had a space just equal to 12 cubic zebos. Other
containers were 10, 100, or 1000 times as large as
the first.

As was stated earlier, Petrie was to find under the
sand that had drifted across the portico of the Temple of
Anubis in ancient Memphis the stone model of a main
commercial wheat measure called an apet by the Egyptians. He measured the inside capacity and found that
the apet was equal in container size to 3000 cubic zebos.

So 4 apets would be equal to 12,000 cubic zebos and would have held a thousand times 1000 kernels of wheat.

In working out their units of weight the Egyptians adopted a wheat-kernel plan. *The heaviness of 1000 kernels of wheat* became the basic small weight. Petrie found what he considered the oldest weights in the world in some ancient tombs in the delta country of Egypt. Made of alabaster rock and fashioned as geometrical figures, they were equal to the heaviness of 200 kernels of Egyptian wheat. Five of these made the small main weight of 1000 *kernel-weights*. (In the English weight plan of today the pound-weight is equal to 7000 grains. The "grain" as a weight unit is but another name for kernel-weight as used by the Egyptians.)

There was another idea about kernel-weights that does not seem to have been used by the Egyptians in a basic way but was given an important role in Phoenician planning. As found by experiment, *10 cubic zebos of cool water had the same weight as 12 cubic zebos of wheat kernels.* Since 12 cubic zebos of wheat held 1000 kernels, 10 cubic zebos of water had the same heaviness as 1000 kernel-weights. The Phoenicians based their container units on the cube of the handbreadth and used the heaviness of that much cool water for the basic weight unit. One great advantage of the new container units was that they could be used both for liquids and for grains, and for other grains beside wheat. The Egyptian containers and kernel-weight units were satisfactory only for wheat.

Three sizes of balance used in Egypt

The Egyptian Balance

The introduction of the maneh and shekel as new weight units did not require any change in weighing devices. The Phoenician cities kept the Egyptian balance with not a single modification of size or design. This type of weighing device used loose weights, and to make the shift from one kind of weight units to another required merely the substitution of a new set of weights for the old.

Today the Egyptian balance is occasionally referred to as a two-pan balance, but that is a duplication of words, since "balance" is from the Latin *bi-lanx* and means "two-pan." The inventive idea behind the device could have come from the arrangement of pole and baskets used in Egypt for carrying weights. The pole balanced upon one shoulder carried a loaded basket at each end; if the baskets were equally heavy the pole was balanced at its center. As pictured upon temple walls, the earliest form of the balance as an instrument was apparently made from a crooked tree limb set on a notched support. In a few centuries the device developed into a fine instrument, accurate in its weighing and handled by a trained operator.

Three sizes are pictured. The largest, about six feet in height, used a strong, well-proportioned wooden beam supported by a wooden stand. Unlike the balance forms of today, the beam did not rotate upon a pivot or wedge. It was held up, instead, by a hammock-like strand of un-twisted linen fibers; any swinging of the beam that would

cause one end to go higher than the other would slightly
twist the fibers, which resisted the beam's motion. Basket-
like pans were attached to the ends of the beams with similar fibers. The weight units used for the weighing were
made from alabaster rock. Stones for the heavier units were
cut in animals forms, and geometrical shapes were given
to the others. A second size of balance was just half as large
as the first one; it was designed for just half as large a total
load. Since the supporting strand of this smaller balance
held the beam up with but half as many fibers, its beam
turned farther under a tiny weight. So the second balance
handled only half as heavy a weight load but did so with
much greater precision.

The third balance was smaller than the others, designed
for a total load that was just a hundredth of that of the
second. This small instrument, kept in a temple room free
from dust and breezes that might disturb the beam's
motion, can be called quite properly the "gold balance."
In Egypt it was used for the weighing of gold, silver, ivory,
ebony, vials of perfume, and crystals of dye material.

In Phoenician times the highly precise gold balance
could be handled only by those who were attached to
the temple. Weight marks placed on a lump of silver or a
piece of ivory after a temple weighing would carry the
sign of the temple also. Another, and less precise, small
balance was made for Phoenician traders by the temple
mechanics of Tyre, Sidon, and Gebal. It was portable,
the beam was removable, and the device could be packed
in a waterproof bag for carrying. Stone weights, kept in

the bag when not in use, were used with the device. With the Phoenicians the capacity of this portable balance was one maneh; one maneh, of course, was 50 shekels. The larger stone weights were stamped.

The Hebrews, as neighbors of the Phoenicians of Tyre and Sidon, made use of the portable balance. Some abuses having developed in connection with its use, this stern admonition appears among the early Hebrew laws as given in Deuteronomy 25:13–15 in the Bible:

"Thou shalt not have in thy bag divers weights, a great and a small.

"Thou shalt not have in thine house divers measures, a great and a small.

"But thou shalt have a perfect and just weight, a perfect and just measure shalt thou have. . . ."

It should be noted that the Phoenician shekel was merely a weight unit in the beginning. In fact the word meant a "weight." That is the use of shekel—a *weight unit*—in the Bible story of Goliath in which the weight of his armor is given. The merchants of Tyre and Sidon, however, were to give the word a different significance. After the discovery of silver in Tarshish, lumps of silver were used in buying and selling, much as money is used today. In one-shekel pieces, each marked with a temple's weighing sign, these "pieces of silver" circulated in all areas where the Phoenicians traded.

The shekels, either as lumps or as strips, had a weight close to one-third that of the silver dollar of the United States. They did not look, however, like the coins of to-

SHEKEL

Coins of the ancient world

day, which have milled edges, and designs covering both faces. The coin was the invention of Croesus, king of a small mountainous country in Asia Minor. When an abundance of silver and some smaller deposits of gold were found in his country he had the metals made into lumps of a single weight and size. He did not have them marked, or a temple sign added, but had each piece of metal set between two dies that flattened the lump as pressure was applied and printed a special design on each side. The idea had two advantages. It tended to discourage the re-

moval of part of the metal, since the rounding off of surfaces and chipping of edges would readily be noticed.
Besides, the coin had an advertising importance that
later kings and industrial cities or countries were quick to
recognize. Names, kings' faces, and commercial designs
have appeared on coins since the time of Croesus. But
the weight of the coin has not been placed upon the design
—an omission that started with Croesus.

Relation Between the Phoenician Weights and Measures and Those of Early England

The maneh of the Phoenicians matched in nature the
skale-weight of early England; each was as heavy as half
a cubic handbreadth of cool water. The Phoenician
shekel as a silver weight corresponded to 10 skeat-weights
coined from silver by the early kings of Saxon England.
So it is evident that the weight plan of the Phoenicians
was, like the other parts of their old measurement system,
so similar in nature to the system of early England that
one must have been derived from the other. But the
Phoenician plan was geared to the Egyptian armstretch
of 73.64 present-day inches, the one of early England to
the armstretch of 79.20 inches. The two systems that were
alike in nature, and both decimal in the relationships of
the units, were thus not alike in size.

The English plan had been brought from the other
side of the North Sea, where it had been in use among the
Germanic and Gothic tribes of north-central Europe. For

centuries these tribes had had no lands touching on the Mediterranean. Yet at some time, somewhere, somehow, the Phoenician measurement system had become known in its entirety to the people of north-central Europe, adopted by them, but redesigned for a longer armstretch. These are the conclusions that seem evident; they would imply a prolonged and intimate contact between the Phoenicians and the European people of these areas. They suggest the enthusiastic influence of some dominant northern chieftain in making over the Phoenician plan to suit the big warriors of his own tribe.

It seems reasonable to suppose that the contacts were made along the northern shores of the Black Sea, where for several centuries the Phoenicians had important trading connections. Animal pelts, amber, and honey were traded there for bronze tools and implements. Apparently the fine harbor occupied by modern Odessa, just east of the mouth of the Dniester River on the north shore of the Black Sea, was the Phoenician headquarters for this trade. It seems probable that this point was used as a shipbuilding center for the entire area, and that the city built beside the harbor was a Phoenician colony of importance.

Odin, a leader of the Goths, may have been the chieftain who directed the adoption of the Phoenician plan. In the Scandinavian Eddas, in which ancient legends have been preserved, there are some that were sung by wandering minstrels untold centuries before they were written down. In the later legends, Odin (also called Weden, Woden, and Wotan) is the central deity of the old northern mythology—the god of crops, ships, and manly warfare. In legends that were not so recent, Odin is a minor god who looks after crops, ships, and personal warfare for the men of the tribe. In the earliest of all the Odin legends, the singer tells the exploits of Odin, mighty chieftain of the Goths, and of how he led the Goths from the banks of the Dniester River across central Europe to the shores of the Baltic.

Such is the report that the historians can give us. Any addition to the story can be but guesswork. Before the time of Odin we can suppose that the Goths were semi-nomadic hunters, living on the products of the chase and the catching of river fish, supplemented with berries that could be dried for the winter and with wild plants whose bulbous roots could be eaten raw or cooked. Life was sometimes pleasant, sometimes hard, depending upon the results of the chase. Then the time came when cattle and sheep were kept in pastures and used to supply meat. Along with that change, grains were grown in plowed fields, and life took on a settled kind of existence as each community made use of the arts of farming. It must be supposed that Odin, by years of contact with the Phoenicians, their home life and crops, and their methods of shipbuilding, guided his tribe away from the semi-nomadic manner of life to one of domesticated cattle, grain crops, and settled living. It can be supposed also that he accepted the Phoenician ways of measurement but objected to the small seats on the ships as the Phoenicians put them in. He wanted big seats for big men, and got them by using a longer armstretch as a measure. That seems reasonable. Perhaps he selected his own armstretch as the new standard; if so, his general size is known, for the proportions of body parts to one another are remarkably simple.

The decimal measurement plan of Odin and the Goths was to follow the slow spread of the new farm life among the peoples that were to be known as Norse and Germans. When the new measures came into use for fields and distances, for products of the harvest and for weights of pelts, the armstretch of Odin lasted on unchanged and so kept the entire measurement plan unchanged also. In early England, therefore, the plan that came with the first group from across the North Sea might already have been over a thousand years old, since the supposed contacts of Odin with the Phoenicians could have been made about 1000 B.C.

III

With Accent on the Foot: the Greek Story

Into the decimal plan of lengths of early England a new measure, the English foot, was introduced about seven centuries ago. Its presence upset the simplicity, for the foot was not divided into tens and hundreds and had no decimal relations to larger length units. This foot was not an English idea. The Romans, however, had used such a unit, taken from the Greeks, who had devised it in the first place. The division of the English, Roman, and Greek foot measures into 12 parts can be traced back to ancient Babylon and its length plan of about the year 1000 B.C.

Mahis and Thumb-breadths

Ancient Babylon, though separated from Egypt by hundreds of miles of desert and connected commercially only by long caravan routes to Tyre or other Phoenician cities, used in connection with a sea route from Phoenicia to the Nile country, made use of the decimal armstretch plan

that Egypt had developed. It also used the Egyptian
balance, in its three sizes, and the idea of counting wheat
kernels by thousands in devising the container sizes of
wheat measures. Decimal divisions, however, were not
always followed, 60 and 120 being used more frequently
than 50 and 100.

As has previously been stated, Phoenicia produced a
new plan for container sizes and weights, about 1200 B.C.
This plan selected some length unit, used the cube of that
as the container unit, and the heaviness of the water filling it as the weight unit. The basic length that was chosen,
as we have already noted, was the tefah, or handbreadth;
the heaviness of a cubic tefah of water was to be 100
shekels. The plan had definite advantages over earlier
arrangements for container sizes and weights.

About 1000 B.C., Babylon put into commercial use a
new plan for containers and weights built around the
same principles as those of the Phoenicians but making
use of a different length unit. The Babylonians divided
the Egyptian mahi or forearm length into halves and used
the half-mahi for container sizes and weights. The half-
mahi itself was divided into 10 parts of thumb-breadth
size; and 10 half-mahis, as a cord length, seems to have
taken the place of the Egyptian cord of twice that length
used for general building. The cubic half-mahi, as a container measure, was used for both liquids and grains. Its
smallest divisions were 1000 cubic thumb-breadths. The
heaviness of the water filling the cubic half-mahi was

counted as 1000 *bekas*, each beka being the heaviness of a cubic thumb-breadth of water. There were two smaller weight units. The *scruple* was a tenth of the beka, while the beka was also counted as 200 grains, a *grain* being the weight of a kernel of wheat. This grain was very nearly the kernel-weight of early Egypt.

In its entirety, this decimal plan of Babylon may be counted as the best plan of the ancient world. It was completely decimal in its relationships, and completely logical in its interrelations of units of length, container size, and weight. By contrast, the Phoenician plan had the maneh as the heaviness of *half* a cubic tefah (handbreadth) of water and divided the maneh into 50 shekels or 50,000 gerahs; and the plan of early England, following that of the Phoenicians, had the skale-weight as the heaviness of *half* a cubic handbreadth of water.

The Babylonian measures for grains, liquids, and the weight of the beka and scruple reached the western shores of Asia Minor by following the caravan routes. A few centuries before, the units of the Phoenicians had come into use in all Phoenician trading ports along the Greek shores and those of the Black Sea. In Greece itself the plans overlapped. The confusion of systems, however, was not excessive since 5 zebos (fingerwidths) of the Egyptians and Phoenicians was exactly equal to 4 thumb-breadths by the Babylonian plan, and 100 shekels had the exact weight of 64 bekas.

Getting the Foot In

In the dim days of an earlier history the Greeks had lived north of the land that is known as Greece today. About the year 1100 B.C. an important shift of European climate had forced these people out of their old homelands. Seeking new pastures for their flocks of sheep, they had fought their way, grimly and bitterly, down into the peninsula which they were to call Hellas and which we know as Greece. Those who sought to oppose them were annihilated or enslaved, their lands taken, their homes burned. For a century or more the struggle for the possession of the land extended farther and farther to the south, crossed to the large island of Crete, then spread to the small islands that dot the Aegean Sea and to the Asian shore. Eventually the fighting stopped. The former inhabitants either had escaped with their possessions by sea or had been crushed.

The Greeks first came into contact with the Phoenician traders along the western shore of the Black Sea, in a region near the mouth of the Danube River. Though the Greeks had few goods to give in exchange, they managed to obtain some knives, swords, and helmets. Finding it easier to get these things from the traders by thieving and trickery than by trading, they became pirates. Athens was started as a pirate lookout, Corinth as a den of robbers. Eventually the Phoenicians ceased to enter the Black Sea waters or even the Aegean Sea. Shifting their trade routes, they sailed out to the western Mediterranean, there to build a great trading empire.

In early Greek writings there is abundant evidence that the Greeks had picked up the Phoenician length plan that was built around the Egyptian nent (armstretch) according to a decimal system. Greek words took the place of Phoenician words, but no change was made in the plan itself. Then, somewhat later, units appear that were not in the earlier plan. The Greeks were working out a length system of their own. They wanted something for fighting men—and that was what they got.

Their starting point was the mahi or forearm length used by Egyptians, Phoenicians, and Babylonians. The Greeks found that three mahis matched in length their double-step as used in marching. They called this 3-mahi length a *bema*. It was used in military maneuvers in this way. The men would march along, stamping with one foot as they went, in a sort of battle rhythm. The leader would pound on his shield after every 10 bemas, pound twice after every 100, and three times after every 1000. He would also call out "Kilo" for the thousand-bema length; *kilo* was their word for "thousand."

The bema and kilo were not enough for a full plan of lengths. Since the length of a soldier's foot was very nearly a fifth of his double-step stride, they put in the new length-unit of *pous,* which was to be of such a size that 5 pous-lengths made a bema-length. Pous was their word for "foot." There was no need to devise a still smaller unit, since either the zebo (fingerwidth) of the Phoenicians

Greek soldier stepping off a *bema* step

or the thumb-breadth of the Babylonian plan could be used. The pous was 15 zebos or 12 thumb-breadths.

Two other changes were made by the Greeks. The cloth-measure used by the Phoenicians was 50 zebos long; the Greeks shortened theirs by 5 zebos so it would be just 3 pous-lengths long. This was their cloth-yard. The fathom as used by the Phoenicians was the nent of 100 zebos; the Greeks shortened theirs to 90 zebos so that it would be equal to 6 pous-lengths. None of the various units that were thus introduced by the Greeks—the pous, the kilo, the bema, the cloth-yard, the fathom—was awkward in size or inconvenient in use. Their fault lay in the fact that

the simplicity of a great decimal arrangement was now
largely destroyed.

The weight plan of early eastern Greece was built upon
the Babylonian plan in which the heaviness of the cubic
half-mahi of water was put down as 1000 bekas or 10,000
scruples or 20 times 10,000 grains. Since the half-mahi was
10 thumb-breadths, this meant that the heaviness of a
cubic thumb-breadth of water was one beka, or 10 scruples, or 200 grains. Keeping the idea but modifying the
arrangement, the Greeks took the heaviness of a *cubic
pous* of water as the center of their plan. The pous was
equal to 12 thumb-breadths, so the cubic pous was 1728
cubic thumb-breadths. The heaviness of each cubic
thumb-breadth of water was counted, as in the Babylonian
plan, as one beka or 10 scruples or 200 grains. For the
cubic pous the result was 1728 bekas, or 17,280 scruples,
or 20 times 17,280 grains. The Babylonian arrangement
was fully decimal in nature, the Greek one was awkward
and confusing. For smaller units, the Greek plan was as
follows:

17,280 scruples were divided into 60 *litra-weights;*
each litra-weight was divided into 12 *twelfth-weights;*
each twelfth-weight was equal to 8 *dram-weights;* and
each dram-weight was equal to 3 scruples or 60 grains.

Solon and the Big Foot

Another part of the Greek story of weights and measures tells of a plan devised by Solon, the Greek, after he

became archon of Athens. The tale has a dramatic beginning. In the year 594 B.C. Athens was seething with
excitement. Angry mobs of hungry people were in the
streets. The city's harbor, the finest in eastern Greece,
was empty of boats—and had been for months. Commerce
had gone elsewhere. The city was bankrupt. In despera-
tion the leaders had decided to call in Solon, a noted merchant of the Greek city of Miletus, and a world traveler.
How it must have hurt their Athenian pride to beg aid
of a merchant! Solon consented to come if made archon
and given dictatorial powers.

One of Solon's first acts was to suggest a commercial
confederacy of the four Greek cities of Athens, Miletus,

Solon

Rhodes, and Corinth. All of them had similar problems to meet. He suggested that the cities act as a unit in developing new markets and offering new products. Their greatest competitors were the Phoenician traders; the Greeks could learn something from studying the methods of these traders. The Phoenicians used pieces of silver as a convenient and practical way of carrying on foreign purchases; the Greeks should do that too.

It appeared to Solon that the four cities would do well to develop a distinctive measurement system that would be unlike that of the Phoenicians, yet be so adjusted to the Phoenician plan as to permit easy and accurate exchange of such units as those of silver weights. When completed, Solon's plan met both objectives. The Greeks counted by fours, instead of by tens, so that for lengths the plan of Solon was as follows:

4 fingerwidths	were	a palm-width;
4 palm-widths	were	a foot-length.

For additional units, the new forearm length was 6 palm-widths and the new military double-step was 3 forearm lengths.

For a main unit of weight the new plan made the heaviness of a cubic palm-width of water exactly equal to the Phoenician maneh of 50 shekels, or to 32 bekas of the Babylonian plan. To perfect the weight arrangement the Athenian fingerwidth had to be *slightly* smaller than the zebo (fingerwidth) of the Phoenicians. The actual reduction was close to half a part in a hundred.

No attempt whatever was made to have any of the new units exactly equal to a corresponding unit in the earlier Greek plan. The same names would be used, but the *daktylos* (fingerwidth) of Athens was not exactly the same in length as the earlier daktylos, the pous (foot-length) of Athens was a fingerwidth longer than the older one, the bema (double-step length) of Athens was five fingerwidths longer than the other bema, and the units of container sizes and of weights were correspondingly different also. Solon had the old units made illegal in the four Greek cities of which we have spoken. The rest of Greece responded by making the Solon units illegal. That was a situation that might have continued indefinitely had it not been for Alexander the Great, two hundred years later. As his victorious army swept out of Thrace across Greece, then on into Asia as far as India, and into Africa as far as certain oases west of Egypt, he had the needs of the fighting men supplied according to the measures of Solon. So the units of Athens, Miletus, Rhodes, and Corinth became the legal ones for the entire Alexandrian world.

The Romans Do Some Compromising

The story now moves from Greece to Rome. This fortress city on the Tiber River had as its neighbors the rich and prosperous Etruscans. These neighbors used the measurement plan of early Greece that was built about the pous. The people of early Rome knew no other plan. When, in the centuries that marked the early history of the Romans, their armies conquered the territory that is now included in Italy, Spain, and France, the units of length, container size, and weight went along. They were used for military distances and for handling army supplies.

At a later period of history the conquests of the Roman armies took in much of the old Alexandrian world. Since the units of Greek measurement in this territory were those of Solon, for a time the measuring of distance, container size, and weight was different in the eastern part of the Roman dominions from that in the western part. Some decision had to be made as to which plan should be used officially for the Roman armies everywhere. Emperor Augustus (who reigned from 27 B.C. to 14 A.D.) decided in favor of the Solon measures and weights.

In the west the change to Solon units applied legally only to official and army usage. No interference took place in reference to the use of early Greek units in local matters. But to bring some harmony to the common and legal ways of handling distance and weight, two changes were enforced. The first change decreased the size of the daktylos or fingerwidth of the early Greek plan just enough to make it exactly as large as the fingerwidth of Solon's arrangement. That change was slight.

The other change had to do with weight units. The names of early Greek units were kept but their sizes were altered, while a new unit was added to Solon's plan, with its size so calculated as to let it fit smoothly into either modified weight plan. That added unit was the new twelfth-weight, called the *uncia of weight* by the Romans, since uncia was their word for "twelfth." In connection with Solon's weights, 16 uncias of weight made a *pondus,* 60 pondus-weights was the heaviness of a cubic foot of cool water. By the other plan of weights as modified, 12 uncias of weight made a *libra,* and 80 libra-weights was the heaviness of a cubic foot of cool water. Since the cubic foot of Solon was used for the water in both arrangements, there was no lack of harmony. So it was that the Roman provinces in western Europe learned to count weights in two different but not discordant sets of units— the pondus of 16 uncias and the libra of 12 uncias.

Effects of the Fall of Rome

AN INTERLUDE IN THE STORY OF WEIGHTS AND
MEASURES

The fall of Rome and the collapse of the western Roman
Empire are events that mark the close of ancient history.
The resulting inrush of Gothic fighting men, who followed
the Roman military highways to take military possession
of the various provinces, begins a new period of history
sometimes called the Dark Ages.

The invading chiefs, accustomed to measuring land in
armstretches, furlongs, and acres, kept to these measures.
Accustomed to giving container sizes in measure-fulls,
tankard-fulls, and tuns, they adhered to such container
sizes. Used to skale-weights and hundredweights, they
kept on using these units. The people in the conquered
provinces, as serfs of the Gothic chieftains, were forced
to bring their measurements into harmony with those of
their overlords. In Spain, for example, 18 common feet
made the builder's rod-length of the invader; the Roman
common foot had to be changed slightly to make this adjustment. In northern Italy the chief of the Lombards com-

pelled a slight increase in the legal foot of the Roman plan whereby 9 Roman fathoms of 6-foot size had the exact length of 8 armstretches by the Gothic plan. In France, one adjustment was demanded by the Frank chieftain of the north, a different one by the Burgundian chief of the area lying farther to the south. As the result of such forced adjustments, several footlengths came into use in what had been the western part of the Roman Empire.

The following countries were not affected by this initial need of adjustment to Roman units: England, Germany, Holland, Denmark, Sweden, and Norway. These areas retained the units of the Gothic tribes.

About seven centuries after the fall of Rome a new industrial era began in Germany and nearby sections. Trade increased, larger boats were built, cities purchased free-city rights from kings, cooperative trade organizations were formed, craftsmen banded together to form guilds, fairs were started and placed on a continuing basis as a way of increasing sales. As wealth and prosperity developed in the industrial cities, a great cathedral-building period began in which cities vied with each other over the heights of steeples and the richness of ornamentation.

One effect of this trade expansion was the insertion of a "foot-length" into the measurement plan of the German cities. The effect was unfortunate, for this unit did not fit in a decimal way into the simple Gothic system. But once it was in, other units of the Roman type followed. The final result of this adjustment was a non-decimal arrangement of units of assorted sizes. England, too, got a "foot-length" in this industrial period—though its foot was not of German size, and other features of the adjusted non-decimal arrangement were matched in name but not in size by German units. It is the English story of measurement that will be followed.

IV

The Rebuilt Measures
of England

In the year 1066, William the Conqueror and his knights in full armor, on war horses, met the stout foot soldiers of Harold the Saxon on the battleground of Hastings. William and his followers spoke the Norman-French dialect, they made measurements in French units, and they fought in French style. Harold and his men spoke Anglo-Saxon English, measured with the units of early England, and fought in the hand-to-hand style familiar to all Angles and Saxons. The battle was decisive and William became ruler of England. Eventually, words from Norman-French were to become part of the English speech. Eventually, too, one measurement unit of the French plan would be inserted in the old system of early England. But it would not have a French size, for it was going to be designed in a way that was new.

The "king's rod"

The King's Rod

Flinders Petrie in examining the buildings of an older England discovered that the second stone structure of Westminster Abbey, added in the time of Henry III, the seventh king after William, had been constructed with a builder's rod different from that used in early English times. The people of England called the new one the *king's rod*. Actually the new rod was neither longer nor shorter than the old one. The divisions, however, were different; apparently the old cuts and marks on the rod had been planed off and new cuts and marks put on. As was stated earlier, there had been a total of 200 thumb-breadths. That number on the king's rod had been changed to 198, with 12 of these making the new unit of length that Henry would call the *English foot*. The new thumb-breadth, which the king called an uncia (for "twelfth"), was known to the English workmen as an *unch*. We write the word as *inch*. That is how the foot got its size and the inch its name; and because 198 is just one per cent smaller as a number than 200, so the old thumb-breadth is just one per cent smaller as a measure than the inch.

It does not seem to have been long before the 3-foot yard became a part of the English plan of measurement, displacing the old wand as a cloth measure. The yard was equal to 36 inches, whereas the wand had been 40 thumb-breadths—a considerable difference in length. The yard doubtless came into common use first of all in London and among the followers of the court who kept to French clothing materials and fashions. Within a century the use of the yard became so common that Parliament acted to make the use of the wand illegal.

Londinium and the New London

There is little doubt that Henry III in looking at the ris-ing stone structure of the second portion of Westminster Abbey was satisfied that the inserting of the foot and inch into the building rod's length had been a great improvement. Others in and around London may have agreed. But when, about the year 1300, it was evident that the entire container and weight plan of early England would have to be changed because of that foot, people may have wondered. Doubtless there were some at that time who would be saying that the decision to crowd in the foot-length had been a grave blunder. But blunder or no, the changes in container and weight units had to be planned for, now that the foot was in. The task of deciding upon a possible arrangement of new units fell to the merchants, not to king or Parliament, and the merchants would be those of London, the largest and busiest of England's cities.

The year 1300, of which we have been speaking, was six and a half centuries ago. London at that time had a population of about forty thousand people. It was then, as a city, both very old and rather young. The Romans had built a fortress city there on the top of a flat-topped cliff of clay that rose fifty feet above the waters of the Thames River. A long wooden bridge, beginning at the top of the clay cliff, rose high over the water of London harbor to connect the city with the southern bank of the river. At the base of the cliff were the landing docks for the Roman boats, and from the docks ran the steep twisting roads to the top up which the Roman supplies were moved on their way to the warehouses. As a fortress city, the place, named Londinium by the Romans, was surrounded by a strong wall. Through its well-guarded gates ran the military roads that connected London to all southern strategic points.

After the Romans left Britain and the Saxons came to southern parts of the great island, the city of London lay deserted for centuries. In that period of desertion, London Bridge, giving access to the city from the south, was rotting into decay. The brick warehouses along the narrow Roman passageways had crumbled to rubble. Parts of the Roman wall were down and the heavy city gates sagged on their rusty hinges.

Then came a rebirth. It took an outsider and a military man to see the location as one for a great, unconquerable city. This outsider was Knut the Dane—or Canute the Dane, as some historians write his name. From 1017 to his death in 1035 he was king of both England and Denmark, and he made London his capital. He saw the city as a great seaport of the future, whose magnificent natural harbor, beyond reach of Atlantic gales and scoured of mud by the movement of the tides, was large enough to hold the boats of the world. He saw it also as a trading center that would draw to itself the sea routes of western Europe and the stream and highway routes of all England. In later centuries, slowly, those dreams came true.

By the year 1300—which was 265 years after the death of Knut the Dane—the city had grown sufficiently in population to fill the space within the old Roman wall. But the old rubble of crumbling brick had never been wholly cleared away to make room for better streets to the cliff top. The harbor now was busier than even in Roman times. The skiffs and scows of local fishermen threaded the area about the inner wharves. In the deeper water below London Bridge would be seen the high-pooped freighters from the Flemish cities across the English Channel. There would be dignified English merchant ships. There would also be galleys out of Venice or Genoa that could hold five times the cargo of any English boat, and had five times the crew. Mixed with the others, there would be weatherbeaten trading vessels from the North Sea and the Baltic bringing in furs and amber and salt fish.

London would be a particularly busy place whenever the long Mediterranean galleys and the tall ships of Spain came sailing in from the sea. In the cargoes to be unloaded would be rare spices from the islands beyond India, perfume in tiny glass vials, and brightly colored dyes from Damascus. There would be soft leather and beautiful silk, linen and velvet, broadcloth and brocaded stuff. But the city did not depend wholly upon outsiders for the products offered in the shops. Its own workers made and decorated every kind of apparel from the girdle that held a knight's sword to the silken hood and veil of a lady. Few places were busier than the shops of leather workers. The shoemaker, for example, would make up the shoes for a customer by hand, using the leather he had himself selected. Such a hand-sewed pair of shoes, made of well-tanned leather, would wear a long time and could be patched and mended many times before being outgrown. What a variety of shoe types would be offered! The shoemaker could make riding boots, leather shoes, slippers, sandals, clogs, and pattens. He could make up shoes with the leather on it dyed, stamped, or gilded. Shoe tops could be of cloth, silk, morocco, or velvet. Soles could be of leather, wood, cork, or even iron.

The food for the forty thousand people of London came largely from the outside. The cattle market, beyond the city wall, was open once a week for cattle, pigs, and sheep driven in from outlying farms. Once a week there would be poultry for sale, and other country products such as butter, cheese, honey, and wild fruit. On any day but Sunday there would be fresh fish at the fishmarket by the river and fresh bread at the bakeshops.

England was not then a rich country. There were but few minerals for export—some tin, some iron, some lead. But the country had one product that was in great foreign demand. The wool sheared from English sheep ranked with the best in all Europe. London was the natural center by which the wool reached foreign buyers, and once a year bales of clipped wool and bundles of sheepskins with the wool left on would come in by lane and highway to London. Waiting for the wool would be buyers representing the Flemish weavers or the fine-cloth makers of the great Italian cities of Florence and Milan.

That is the picture that would be seen had we strolled along the streets of London in the year 1300. The city was not a great place in comparison with the large commercial cities of that time. Its business was slight as compared to the products that passed across the counters of Bruges and Venice, Cordova and Genoa, Alexandria and Constantinople. But London was England's largest city and so was important in 1300. Another feature gave it extra importance: London had a special charter from the king that, among other things, permitted it to set up trade regulations and to establish commercial standards. Those provisions were to be important to the story of English measurement.

Aver-de-peis

In the year 1303 the merchants of London, by virtue of the provisions in their charter, put into commercial use a weight plan of their own contriving. The plan had a main unit called *pound* and another, one-sixteenth as heavy, called *ounce*. Both terms were slightly modified forms of the Roman words "pondus" and "uncia." This pound, known today throughout the English-speaking world as *the* pound, was called, in the beginning, the *aver-de-peis* pound, from the Norman French expression for "weight of goods." The spelling now given of *avoirdupois* was actually in error, as it gave the phrasing a Parisian French form, though Paris had had nothing to do either with the weight or its naming.

It is not strange that the London merchants wanted a weight unit like the pound, nor is it difficult to understand why they preferred that the pound of England should be different in weight from the pound of the great Italian

A fourteenth-century London merchant using avoirdupois weight units

commercial cities, or of Spain, or of the German cities of Cologne and Lübeck. Yet in the actual designing of their new units the merchants made no attempt to be original. The German cities had used the idea that a cubic foot of cool water was to be counted as having the heaviness of 1000 ounces. The London merchants used that idea. Since the German foot was equal to 12⅜ English inches, their ounce was somewhat heavier than the London ounce. With 16 ounces to the pound, *each* plan made the heaviness of its cubic foot of water equal to 62½ pounds. The German pound was, of course, heavier than the London pound.

By a matter of chance the English pound was very nearly the size of another weight unit of commercial importance. This was the pound of the Italian cities, which was called a *libra*. Also, the English ounce was very nearly the weight of the Italian ounce, which was called an *onzia*. As a result of the close similarities of size, *li* or *lb* came to be used as abbreviations both for the English pound and the Italian libra; *oz* came into use both for the English ounce and the Italian onzia. Oddly enough, lb. and oz. still persist as our abbreviations for these units, though the Italian units were discontinued a century and a half ago.

One result of the merchants' efforts in getting the pound weight was a clever adjustment of the new weight and the old skale-weight of England. This affected the handling of the half-hundredweight, a unit used by communities throughout England for the weighing of bales of sheep-skins. This unit was retained in both size and name, but was to be marked "56 li," meaning that it was to be counted as 56 pounds, not as 50 skale-weights. The stone was also retained, without change in size or name; it was to be marked "14 li." In fact the definition of the pound was to be as follows:

The avoirdupois pound is to be one-fifty-sixth of the weight of the half-hundredweight standard of Alfred the Great as kept in the Exchequer at Westminster.

When Edward III, about the year 1350, had the standards for the yard and foot added to the Exchequer list of standards, he did not modify the half-hundredweight except to have it marked "56 li."

For the farm people of England, the old tun-weight also remained, unchanged in weight or name. It had been 2000 skale-weights; it was now marked as "2240 li." Today we use the spelling "ton-weight" and refer to the weight itself as the *long ton*.

But what about the other way of finding the weight of the new ounce and pound—that is, by using the idea that a cubic foot of cool water is to be 1000 ounces, with 16 ounces to the pound? Do the results of the two methods agree? This other method is good, but it does not lead to perfect results. Cool water filling a cubic foot of space lacks one-half per cent of being exactly a thousand avoirdupois ounces in weight. By the same small per cent, 16 cubic feet of cool water just misses a weight of exactly 1000 avoirdupois pounds.

Eventually, England became accustomed to the use of the new units. In 1502—two centuries after the introduction of the units by the London merchants—a writer named Arnold put down in his *Chronicles* the following statement about the weighing of goods in England. The *Oxford English Dictionary* has kept his spelling forms in quoting the passage under the heading of "avoirdupois":

"By haberty peyse weyghts is boughte and solde alle maner of marchaundice as is used to be solde by weyght and is of a weyght therby xvi vuncia make a pound and C and xij li is an C."

As to the meaning, his "haberty peyse" was for "aver-de-peis." The closing portion is to be read, "16 ounces make a pound and 112 li is a hundredweight."

The Pint of London

Soon after the new pound went into use in London, another measurement problem presented itself. This had to do with the wine-handling trade. After 1300 the transportation of wine from southern France to the port of London became a lucrative business. Rather small English sailing vessels were used and the wine was handled in kegs or barrels made by London coopers.

In southern France the measurement plan for wine followed an old Roman procedure. The heaviness of a cubic foot of *water* when divided by 60 gave their pondus; wine weighs a little less than water, so a container size that would hold just a pondus-weight of *wine* would have to be a little larger than one-sixtieth of a cubic foot. This container size was called a *pint;* its capacity was a pondus weight of wine. The merchants of England adopted the plan, dividing their cubic foot of liquid space into 60 parts. They had known, of course, that a cubic foot of water weighed 62½ pounds; that idea had been used in their weight plan. What they had not known, perhaps, was that wine, on the average, was just heavy enough so that a cubic foot of it weighed 60 pounds. So the English *pint-of-wine* or *London pint* was made just large enough to hold a pound of wine by being made a sixtieth of a cubic foot in size.

The rest of the wine-container system was simple. Each barrel was made to hold 250 pints of wine—two pints of

air space, in addition, being left above the wine to pre-
vent bursting from expansion in the heat of the sun. Eight
barrels had a total capacity of 2000 pounds of wine. This
amount was called a *wine-ton* or *London ton*. To get
around the situation that came from the use of the ton-
weight of 2240 pounds by most of the country, the London merchants explained that their ton of 2000 pounds
was for the wine and did not take in the heaviness of the
eight oak barrels, with a weight of 30 pounds each. The
total of wine and barrels was 2240 pounds; this was the
exact weight of the old ton. So the Londoners called their
wine-ton by such names as short ton and net ton, and used
the terms long ton and gross ton for the other. To them the
tonnage of a boat meant the tons of wine it could safely
carry, though it was to mean to others the long tons of
any kind of merchandise the boat could transport safely.

The Ounce-of-Troyes

Three quarters of a century before the introduction of
the English pound and ounce, a system of weight units
of foreign origin had come into limited use in London and
in a few other ports of England. Known today as the *troy*
system of weights, these foreign units were to dominate
all weighing made in the shops of the goldsmiths, silversmiths, jewelers, and druggists, since boxes of such weights,
in sets, were being supplied by the manufacturers of the
precision balances used in such shops. Nürnberg was the
manufacturing center for these balances, and the weights

supplied with each instrument were those used in such other industrial cities as Lübeck, Cologne, and Bruges. The German *onze,* or *troy ounce,* was a highly important unit in this plan.

Lübeck, in this same general period of time, began the minting of silver coins containing 95 per cent silver and 5 per cent copper, the copper giving strength to the silver, which by itself is too soft for coin usage. Twenty silver pennies had the weight of one onze. Minted in ample supply and always keeping to a constant weight and even purity, the coins of Lübeck became common in all western Europe.

In the city of London, the merchants of Lübeck had a special marketplace at the side of the river near the foot of London Bridge, where goods from the Baltic Sea regions or manufactured products from German cities were traded for the metals and wool of southern England. Sometimes silver pennies were used in connection with the trading. To the Londoners these outsiders were *Easterners* or *Easterlings;* the second word, when shortened, became *Sterlings.* The Lübeck coins were called sterling silver, the onze as a weight unit was the ounce-sterling, the larger pund (pound) was the pound-sterling. When England, in time, adopted the coinage plan of Lübeck, it adopted also the silver-copper formula for the coin silver and retained the names of sterling silver and pound-sterling. In England those old expressions are still kept.

In a few decades the ounce-sterling would be more often

referred to as the ounce-of-Troyes. That was the period in history when the city of Troyes, on the plains of Champagne to the northeast of Paris, became the central point for the fairs of Champagne. These fairs were held every year for a century and a half and, in their time, were the greatest in all western Europe. To the booths of Troyes, that were thrown open for a six-week period of operation twice a year, came traders, with their goods, from all parts of Europe. Even from distant Constantinople (Byzantium), the old Greek city near the Black Sea, the traders came, their packs filled with spice or drugs or rare perfumes, weighed in terms of the grains, scruples, and drams of ancient Greece.

In the booths of the goldsmiths, silversmiths, and jewelers at the fairs there would be on display gold from mines in Asia Minor that had reached Troyes through Byzantium and had been weighed in Byzantine weights. There would be silver from the mines of southern Germany, brought by way of the cities on the Rhine, weighed in the units of the German industrial cities. There would be amber from the Baltic weighed in those same German weights. There would be booths also where the fine cloth of the Flemish cities would be shown—cloth that might be bought with the silver coins of Bruges. What a terrible mixture of weight units this would appear to indicate! That was not the case, however. There was only one ounce-weight. The ounce-of-Byzantium was the same as the ounce-sterling of Lübeck and the German cities, and Troyes on the plains of Champagne used that same ounce for gold, silver, drugs, and products of the marketplace. So the term ounce-of-Troyes came to be the usual name given by the English buyers at the fairs to the old unit that had, in ancient times, been the twelfth-weight of early Greece.

To conclude the English story of weights, the aver-de-peis pound and ounce, as developed in 1303, were first introduced at a time when the outside weight plan was already well established in London for gold, silver, drugs, and luxury items. The aver-de-peis weights were for commoner, bulkier, and heavier goods. As might be expected, there came a time when some merchant was quite understandingly in doubt as to whether to weigh a piece of mineral, for example, in terms of ounces-of-Troyes or in terms of ounces aver-de-peis. To meet the difficulty, Parliament passed an Act that required the use of the Troyes (Troy) weights for gold, silver and drugs. That law remained on the statute books of England until less than a century ago.

The Opening of a New World

The changes made in the English weight and measurement units through the insertion of the foot-length came in that period of cathedral building and industrial expansion in western Europe that has been called the craftsman period. In that period, as has been stated, London was not a city of outstanding world importance, nor England a great industrial nation.

In 1492 came the discovery of America by Columbus, and that brought immense changes in commerce and trade. Within a century the great Italian cities of Venice and Genoa lost commercial importance to cities facing out on the Atlantic. Dutch Amsterdam grew in size and wealth, Paris prospered, London's harbors were busier than ever before.

There was great excitement in those days over news of Spanish gold, of fortunes made as the result of but a single ship's voyage to Ceylon or the Spice Islands, of strange and wonderful places that had been discovered.

There was excitement too as groups of men and women set out to establish colonies in newly discovered lands. Along with the excitement and achievements of those days, there developed in men everywhere a new boldness of thought, a new breadth of vision, a new zest for striking changes. In the field of weights and measures the mental adventuring would, in part, be directed toward the desire to extend measurement to take in the round earth and all its parts.

V

Some Adventures in
Measurement

In the period from 1600 to 1800 several happenings in the field of measurement were of outstanding importance. The first of these occurred in 1624—four years after the landing of the Pilgrims at Plymouth—when Edmund Gunter of England announced that he had invented a surveying instrument, and a measuring device to use with it, that would permit the lands of the New World to be surveyed rapidly and accurately and with little calculation effort.

Gunter and the Acre

Gunter was a mathematician, an expert instrument maker, a gifted thinker. He was born in Hertfordshire. When Edmund was a teenager, his father, a schoolmaster, thought him incurably lazy. Instead of working or playing in the way of most boys, young Edmund preferred to sit by himself for hours at a time on a hill overlooking the sea. Sometimes he would be shaping a bit of driftwood with the blade of his knife, apparently quite idly. His father assumed that he was dreaming of the sea, and he was. But in those dreams the lad would not think of himself as the captain or mate. He was always the navigator. When the clouds obscured the sun and not an island was in sight, or when the night stars could not be seen and the compass did not point toward the exact north, or when the wind blew steadily toward a rocky shore that he could not see, what would he, the navigator, do? One can believe that, not knowing the answers to his own questions, he asked the sailors by the docks how the navigator did his work. They must have told him that navigation was a hard job, requiring many calculations, and that sometimes the answers to the calculations would be wrong, and a ship would be lost.

It is known that the lad obtained a book on navigation and another on logarithms, and studied them, by himself. It is also known that he made for himself a special ruler that was not divided into inches and parts of an inch but was marked to show the logarithm values for the numbers. With this log-ruler he did not need to look up the logarithm values out of tables. When he wanted to multiply two numbers he added the logarithm values of the numbers by marking one value, then sliding the rule along to put down the other value. That gave him the answer to the problem and he could read the number for the answer from the rule. Today's engineer uses the same idea in the slide rule; but he uses two log-rules, just alike, that he slides past each other in making multiplications.

Gunter, when he became a man, invented a bowl-like device known to seamen as a "gunter." Made of bronze, it was long used by navigators to avoid many of the calculations needed in finding a ship's location at sea. But an even greater contribution to the field of measurement came from his invention for surveying. As a boy, he had, for a time, been greatly interested in surveying. But the subject was not a thrilling one in the England of that day. The lands had been laid out in furlongs and acres so long before, that no one knew who had done the measuring or when. But the situation in America was to be quite different. The reports of discovery that reached England from the lands of the New World told of great expanses that could make the farms of the future. High hills lay to the west of the American settlements. Beyond those hills were vast areas of forest or prairie, large streams, or mighty lakes. Gunter, reading the earliest reports, found a challenge in the situation. Surveyors were going to be needed to lay out the farmlands, to map the shore lines, to cut measurement lanes through the forest. They would need light but strong and accurate equipment. They would need a length measure that would not stretch, and so spoil its accuracy, or rot and decay.

The chain of early England was, as has been noted previously, a length unit represented by a light-weight rope that had knots at a distance of an armstretch apart. The armstretch itself, when used as a measuring stick, was

Gunter's chain for surveying

equal to 10 spans or 100 fingerwidths; Gunter was not aware of these facts, since the armstretch had long been abolished. The chain, however, had not been abolished; and 10 chains were still counted as a furlong, while 10 acres still made a square furlong of land. It was evident to Gunter that surveying would be easier if the chain *length* were divided decimally. The word "chain" made him think of a ship's chain with metal links, so he decided to make his surveyor's chain with 100 iron links. This seemed to build into a perfect plan if the length of the *link* was counted as 10 fingerwidths. To carry out the idea in a practical way was not simple. He had to be able to construct 100 links of light-weight iron, each of exactly the same shape as the others. They would have to be elongated in form and so fashioned that the entire chain could be drawn out to an exact length. They would have to be so designed that they could be assembled in a compact space for carrying, without becoming almost hopelessly intertangled. Gunter succeeded in accomplishing these results, not only for his original chain but for the hundreds of surveying instruments that went to America to be used in opening up the continent.

Edmund Gunter never fulfilled his desire to come to America. He was kept too busy making instruments for the surveyors.

Old Miles and New

One of the units on Gunter's list for the surveyor has not yet been mentioned. It was not one of his creations, but had been in English use since the days of the Norman kings. This was the *common mile*, or *8-furlong mile*, or the mile of 5280 feet.

The word "mile," now so common, was not a word of early England. It was brought in by the Normans, and corresponded to the Roman *mille*, meaning "thousand"; it was the military term for 1000 double steps. The Normans tried to introduce such a length unit in England, but found it virtually impossible to get the people of the English farms and communities to give up the old measurement ways with which they were familiar. As a compromise, the king and his nobles accepted the 8-furlong distance as their military mile. After that, the mile of England no longer represented 1000 double steps.

Between six and seven centuries ago the English *sea-mile* was established as 1000 fathoms, the fathom being equal to six feet. This new mile was longer than the 8-furlong land mile and was shorter than the old thus-hund of early England which, as has been previously noted, was 10 furlongs. In length, 11 of the sea-miles were exactly equal to 10 thus-hunds.

A new chapter in the story of the use of the term "mile" began in modern times when the English captains in sailing the sea lanes of the world discovered something interesting about the earth and its size. They were in the habit of thinking of the earth's circumference as a circle divided into 360 degrees, each degree divided into 60 minutes. They found, by repeated observation and checking, that the sea-mile of 1000 fathoms was very close to one minute of arc on the earth's circumference. This situation was very important to the navigator, and the time was to come when seamen adopted a special mile length of 1013.4 fathoms, calling it the *nautical mile*. This mile was to be just the size of a minute of arc on the circumference of the earth. But really the nautical mile was mis-named; it belonged to the earth, not just to the sea. To the geographer and map-maker it is known today as the *geographical mile*.

An Adventure in Coinage

The tale of measurement now shifts from miles to money. When the United States became an independent country, it developed a coinage plan of its own instead of following the English system. The English plan, modeled after that of Lübeck, was as follows:

$$4 \text{ farthings} = 1 \text{ penny}$$
$$12 \text{ pennies (pence)} = 1 \text{ shilling}$$
$$20 \text{ shillings} = 1 \text{ pound-sterling}$$

As we glance over the numbers 4, 12, and 20, we notice that their product will be 960; so 960 farthings make a pound. Had the numbers been 5, 10, and 20, the pound would have been 1000 farthings. But to reach 1000 in the simplest way the numbers should have been 10, 10, and 10. The new coinage plan of the United States used such a decimal plan for the divisioning of the dollar.

$$10 \text{ mills} = 1 \text{ cent}$$
$$10 \text{ cents} = 1 \text{ dime}$$
$$10 \text{ dimes} = 1 \text{ dollar}$$

The mill was not to be a coin, but the cent, dime, and dollar were. As everyone knows, three additional values have gone in as coins: the 5-cent piece, the quarter-dollar, and the half-dollar. Thomas Jefferson deserves the major praise for the plan, and he received the honor of developing the designs used on the first cent.

One feature of this coinage arrangement was, at this time, quite new. This was the decimal-point way of distinguishing 10 cents from 10 dimes or 10 dollars. Only mathematicians had previously been familiar with the method.

A New French Plan for Weights and Measures

The three developments that have been described—the Gunter decimal plan for the measurement of farm lands, the adapting of the sea-mile to fit the measurement of the earth itself, and the decimal coinage plan of the United States—caught the attention of people everywhere. Men seemed aware for the first time of the advantage of having units counted by tens.

"Perhaps," they would say to each other, "someday a whole system of weights and measures will be set up in which *all* units will be interconnected in a simple decimal manner. How fine that would be." But they themselves could not build such a plan without giving up the foot and pound; and these units, so common and useful, they wanted to keep. So all that anyone seemed able to do was dream.

Before the year 1800, France saw the idea of a new and perfect system of decimally related weight and measurement units change from a dream to reality. A law embodying the features of the new system was passed without an extended debate by the Revolutionary Assembly in the days of the French Revolution. It had the backing of scientific societies, and the details of the plan had been worked out by a small group of outstanding scientists. The basic length unit, around which the entire system of length, container size, and weight had been built in a decimal way, was to be called the *meter*, a name that in French meant merely a "measure." The story of how the meter got its size begins with a report made by the eminent French astronomer Pierre Simon de Laplace. Before a scientific audience he had urged the desirability of expressing the size of a right angle as 100 degrees instead of 90, and the size of each new-sized degree as 100 minutes instead of 60. The right angle would, then, be divided decimally into 100 new-sized degrees or a total of 10,000 new-sized minutes. He was to show that in a mathematical way, and especially in the preparation of tables for angle relationships, the proposed arrangement had outstanding advantages.

It was this idea of a decimally divided right angle that led to the idea of a new sea-mile. By the English plan, the sea-mile was known to be quite close to 1000 fathoms in length; it represented a minute of arc on the earth's surface. The scientists of France proposed a new sea-mile of *exactly* 1000 new fathoms; this mile would be for the new minute on the earth's surface. That new fathom would be the meter. The meter's length would then be defined as a thousandth of a hundredth of a hundredth of a fourth of the earth's circumference.

To get the meter's length from earth dimensions, a surveying line was run across France from north to south, passing through Paris. Astronomers made a careful determination of the same length in terms of degrees. The length of the meter was then calculated. It was reported as equal to 39.37 English inches. A slight error was made; the value should have been 39.40 inches. But before the error was detected, the standard meter bar had been constructed. Its length was not to be changed.

The rest of the metric plan can be surveyed quite quickly. The main container size for grains and liquids was the measure called a *liter;* it represented the space of a cubic decimeter. The heaviness of a liter of water was expressed as 1000 *grams,* the word "gram" meaning in French a "weight." Smaller and larger units than the meter, liter, and gram were related to the basic units in a decimal way. The full plan went into effect in 1799.

A century later, Flinders Petrie was to make the statements about the similarity of the metric plan and the one of early England in the words already quoted on page 23. To elaborate upon Petrie's comments, here are some of the corresponding units of the two plans arranged to show their close relationships:

The wand of early England and of Germany was equal to 39.60 present-day inches; the meter is 39.37 inches.

The handbreadth as a tenth of the wand-length was to correspond to the decimeter as a tenth of the meter.

The old measure-full had been the capacity of a cubic handbreadth; the liter is the corresponding capacity of a cubic decimeter.

The old measure-weight was the heaviness of a cubic handbreadth of cool water; it was equal to 1000 skeat-weights, and 1000 measure-weights made the old tun-weight. The metric kilogram weight is the heaviness of a cubic decimeter of cold water; it is equal to 1000 grams, and 1000 kilograms is the metric *tonne*.

The similarity in length of the wand and the meter must be attributed to chance. The other similarities that run through the two systems must, I believe, indicate that the planners of the metric system were being influenced in their decisions by existing remnants of the old decimal plan to be found at that time in Germany, Holland, Denmark, and the Scandinavian countries.

Spread of the Metric System

The people of France did not accept with readiness the new measurement systems. One situation favored the new arrangement of units, however. Measurement in France was, at that time, in chaotic condition. The foot and fathom in use in Paris did not agree in length with the foot and fathom of southern France. Container sizes were different also. The weight plan, though essentially uniform throughout the country of France, was out of date. It had been established by Charlemagne, the great king of the Franks, for use with coins. These coins had apparently been based upon old worn silver coins of Roman Empire days. The facts indicated that a completely new weight and measurement system would eliminate the difficulties of trying to make a simple plan by tinkering with discordant or outmoded old units.

As was mentioned earlier, the full metric plan went into effect in 1799, and all older plans of weight and measurement units were legally abolished. That was the year Napoleon was named Consul of France. In the war years that followed, the use of metric units for army supplies was strictly enforced. After Napoleon's final defeat the requirements were relaxed. A half-century later the compulsory feature was again enforced as France went to war a second time. Finally, after a total of three-fourths of a century, with the issue decided by the imposition of heavy fines for any use of the older units and by a concerted effort through the schools and business houses in favor of the use of metric units, France fully accepted the decimal system of the meter. The people of France had, at last, discarded the foot.

The metric system story now moves to Germany. In 1871 the German Empire was formed from many kingdoms, duchies, and principalities. At this time the metric system was adopted, its use made compulsory. The merchants and manufacturers of the country were already acquainted with the metric units by long association with their French neighbors, and in the period of great industrial expansion that followed the formation of the Empire, the German workmen found the counting-by-ten arrangements between units both practical and convenient. There was another feature. The main container size and weight unit that a Germany of six centuries before had developed under the leadership of the people of Lübeck were very close to the liter and the half-kilogram of the new plan; changes from the old plan to the new did not, then, involve any great difficulty in the case of container sizes and weights. For the country as a whole, the chief effect of the adoption of the metric units was the complete elimination of the German foot, inch, and yard.

Other nations of northern Europe have followed Germany's example. The reasons that made the shift to metric units not unduly difficult for Germany have operated in their cases.

The Metric System in the United States

In 1866, which was five years before the formation of the German Empire and the establishment of the metric system there, the Congress of the United States passed an Act making the use of metric units legal for this country. The Act applied to the weighing of gold, silver, and drugs as well as to all common weighing; previously there had been troy weights for gold, silver, and drugs, and avoirdupois weights for other things.

This Act was not compulsory in its nature. It merely stated that metric units *could* be used, for they were legal. The American manufacturer could now, if he wished, build machines for customers in which the machine parts were measured in centimeters rather than inches. He could build containers that measured in liters rather than quarts, sell goods by weights in kilograms rather than pounds. It would be entirely legal for the clothmaker to have fabrics woven to meter widths rather than yards. It would be equally legal for county road commissioners to have road signs erected that would give distances in kilometers rather than miles.

It will soon be a century since that United States Act was passed. Throughout that time the use of metric units has made little progress except in scientific work. In that century the country has had a tremendous industrial growth. Growth in science has also been great, but Congress cannot be expected to go beyond the Act of 1866 by making the use of metric units compulsory. Such a legal act would eliminate the inch, foot, yard, fathom, mile, pint, quart, gallon, bushel, ounce, pound, and ordinary ton, as well as require some moderate changes in the furlong, acre, and long ton. The United States has not been willing to make the sweeping change, a situation that will apparently continue in any foreseeable future.

VI

Nineteenth-Century Changes
in English Units

To give greater completeness to the story of the common weight and measure units of England and America, it is necessary to return to the early part of the nineteenth century and say something about what took place in English units after the United States became a separate and independent nation.

That Bushel of Ours

No country in today's world except our own measures liquids with a pint of one size and rice or other grains with a pint of another size, while ours is the only English-speaking country with a bushel that is not equal to eight gallons.

Our bushel—which Petrie has stated is best called the *London bushel*—came to America with the Colonists. It held 64 pints, but those pints were of a very distinctive size. They held more than did the wine-pints of London.

Two facts about the wine-pint and how it was designed have already been mentioned. It was just a sixtieth of a cubic foot in size and, as a result of its size, a pint of wine weighed, on the average, just a pound. The wine-handlers were thus able to use the wine-pint both as a container size and as a weight of this liquid. The situation was very convenient.

In time, the grain dealers wanted a similar plan for their own use. They wanted a grain-pint that would hold just a pound of wheat or barley. Their request was granted. By the London plan, 7 cubic feet of wheat or barley was considered to be just as heavy as 6 cubic feet of wine. A pint that was 7⁄8 as large as the wine-pint would, therefore, hold a pound of grain. That was the plan. There were to be 64 of these *grain-pints* to the bushel, so the London bushel's size was to be 2150.4 cubic inches—as calculated from the fact that 7 cubic feet of space was equal to 6 times 60 pints. In a practical way it may be noted that a tight bin just 7 feet long, 4 feet wide, and 4 feet deep holds exactly 90 bushels.

In America the bushel as *a basket of convenient container size* was used with many farm products beside wheat and barley; the bushel as *a weight unit of 64 pounds of produce* could be used only with these particular grains. In the Colonial stores the grain-pint as one-sixty-fourth of the bushel was used for measuring peas, beans, and rice; for such products the pint did not mean a pound. In those same stores the wine-pint was used for vinegar and molasses; for these liquids the pint did not represent a pound. Also, since the grain-pint was a sixth larger than the wine-pint, the customer would be cheated if peas were measured by the pint used for wine, and the storekeeper would cheat himself by measuring molasses with the pint used for grain.

In England the idea of the pint as a pound of produce was extended to other substances besides wheat, barley, and wine. By 1824 there was in use a beer-pint, and ale-pint and a milk-pint also. In that year, the British Parliament, after due consideration, swept away all the old pints, as well as the old bushels and gallons. A new pint was substituted, with which all pint measurements would be made; eight of these pints made the new gallon; eight of the new gallons made the new bushel. To define the units, the gallon was to be of such a size as to hold exactly 10 pounds of cool water.

All nations of the British Commonwealth adopted this imperial gallon. Canada is one of these nations. In that country 5 gallons of gasoline is just equal to 6 United States gallons; in that country the pints, quarts, gallons, pecks, and bushels of our country are legally prohibited. Their bushel is quite close to ours in size, the exact relations being 129 to 125.

Drams, Scruples, and Pharmacopoeias

The British Weights and Measures Act of 1878 abolished the use of troy and apothecary weights, long used in Britain, but the grain was retained (defined as $\frac{1}{7000}$ of an avoirdupois pound) and the troy, or *fine,* ounce (480 grains) remained the legal unit for weighing precious metals and stones. The troy ounce was also used for coinage purposes. Physicians and pharmacists were required to discontinue the dram and scruple weights of ancient Greece and to adopt instead the weight units of English origin.

Some time was allowed between the time of the passage of the Act and the date when it would be put into effect. Preparations for the change had to be made. The pharmacopoeia—the authoritative guide to the properties and uses of drugs—had to be revised. The dosages that had been given in the old units of weight needed to be recalculated in terms of avoirdupois weights. Drug manufacturers, physicians, pharmacists, and nurses cooperated in making the great change.

About seven years before these happenings, the physicians of Germany, in cooperation with those of France, had revised, just as completely, their own pharmacopoeia for drug usage and permitted dosages when they gave up the troy and apothecary weights in favor of metric units. Here too the preparation for the change was carried through well, the shift from the old units to the new ones being handled successfully.

For the United States there was to be no law that would abolish the troy and apothecary weights, but, as was mentioned before, the use of metric units for such weighing had been permitted by the Act of 1866. The United States pharmacopoeia has, therefore, had a double listing of dosages, one for the old weights, the other for the metric ones. There is now a growing tendency on the part of drug manufacturers, physicians, pharmacists, and hospital attendants to give all dosage weights in metric units. It saves the possible danger that may come from confusing grains and grams in prescriptions. In addition, the metric units are easier to understand and use.

Measurement Trends of the Twentieth Century

A PROGRESS REPORT

The final section of the story of weights and measures relates to the twentieth century, now past its midpoint. As the century advanced there were left in the field of measurement only the two great industrial systems of the foot-and-pound and the meter-and-kilogram.

The situation of two world systems is not expected to change in any foreseeable future. Changes are in progress, however, that relate to improved measurement practices in such a country as ours. These need to be mentioned in order to make the full story complete.

VII

Trends in Measurement Practices

Mikes for the Mechanic

The present century has seen a great increase in the use of decimal fractions in metal work. The trend started with the invention of the micrometer, a simple but highly accurate device by which thicknesses of metal pieces or axle shafts can be measured in tenths, hundredths, and thousandths of an inch. For the metal worker the *mike*, as he called the device, soon became indispensable.

The practice of marking the dimensions of machinery, the sizes of holes, and the location of fittings in a decimal-fraction way, rather than in a common-fraction way, soon followed. Carl M. Johanssen of the Ford Motor Company introduced the plan of indicating all such sizes to one-hundredth of an inch, and found that the workmen had no difficulty in using or interpreting the plan. This "two-place decimal system," as it is called, is used in all automotive plants today and by most of the aircraft industry.

The idea of decimal dividing is now being extended to almost all fields of industry. The engineer's chain, for example, has a length of 100 feet, divided into hundredths as a smaller unit. The capacity of an electric refrigerator is stated today in cubic feet and decimal parts of a cubic foot. The yield of milk by a dairy herd is given in gallons and decimal parts of a gallon, or in pounds and decimal parts of a pound. The automobile odometer on the dash board gives the distance traveled in miles and decimal parts of a mile. The gasoline vending machine indicates the quantity of fuel in gallons and decimal parts of a gallon. We may say then that a shifting from common fractions to decimal fractions is an industrial trend of the time.

Self-registering Scales

The development of numerous forms and types of self-registering devices for measurement and weighing can be noted as a second trend of the times. Normally these devices record values according to decimal fractions. In almost every food market are scales that handle the weighing automatically. The article to be weighed is put on the platform of the scales, and the machine does the rest. When the article is removed, the weight recorder returns to the starting position.

Calculating devices have also been produced that can add, subtract, multiply, and divide. What clever things these devices are! Punch a few buttons, turn a handle, and the arithmetic jobs are done. There will be no need to check the results, since the machine will make no mistakes if the correct buttons are pressed.

There are numerous special forms of calculating machines. The cash register can add up a column of figures and, at the same time, print the amount of each item as well as the value of the total. A special form of mechanism can also provide the proper change for the customer's purchases. The gasoline-vending machine has its calculating mechanism that measures the fuel and determines the cost as the gasoline is flowing. In ways such as these, the self-registering and calculating machines have made tremendous changes in American life.

Experiments in Avoiding Fractions

In spite of the machines, there can still be many calculation problems left for us to do. The calculating machines are expensive devices. If we do not have enough work to keep such a machine moderately busy, we cannot afford it. So in certain work we shall have to do the calculating ourselves or construct a machine of our own. Some of the most bothersome home problems that take in both measurement and calculation seem to be those that have common fractions in them. You may be interested, then, in two home-made devices that are guaranteed to take away some of the measurement and calculation headaches that are met around the home shop and the home farm.

The first of these devices seeks to eliminate the common-fraction difficulties in woodworking and carpentry that come from using a rule with inches marked off by

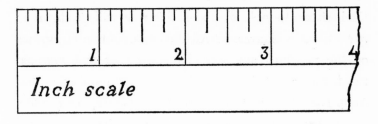

Inch scale

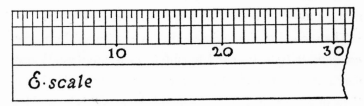

E·scale

eighths and sixteenths. Numbers containing common-fraction values, as such a rule will give, are difficult to add, subtract, multiply, or divide. By a simple attachment the common-fraction values are entirely eliminated. Start with two yardsticks, just alike, whose inches are divided into eighths and sixteenths. Cut both to the length of 25 inches. Leave one unchanged, so that it may be used for comparative purposes. Cut a strip of firm, stiff paper that is just 25 inches long but somewhat narrower than the width of the face of the sticks. This strip is to be cemented to the other yardstick in such a way that the eighth and sixteenth marks may be seen but other inch marks are covered up. Now mark clearly upon the paper the position of every tenth eighth-line, numbering these in order as 10, 20, 30, on up to 200, which is at the stick's end. Call each distance of a one-eighth-inch size an E. The full length will be 200 E's, and one-half the length will be 100 E's.

Each sixteenth-inch length on this rule will go down as
.5 E. What is the result? All the common-fraction values
on the yardstick are now changed either into a whole
number of E's or into a decimal-fraction number ending
in .5. You are to make all measurements with the E-scale,
or transfer lengths from one 25-inch stick to the other, and
notice how the common-fraction troubles disappear.

The second of the home-made devices is called an *acre-
counter*. It is to be used to obtain in a simple and easy
way a knowledge of the number of acres and decimal fractions of an acre in a plot of ground. It does this by making
its measurements in terms of the lengths of early England.
The device is made in triangular shape, of light-weight
material, with a handle at the top of the triangle and a base
made from a strip of wood. Wooden pegs with rounded
tips are set on the under side near each end of the base,
the distance between the two peg centers being the length
of the old armstretch of 79.2 inches. The armstretch distance is marked off into 10 spans. The next decimal divisions would have been made by fingerwidths, but the
two hands, side by side, can be used as a fingerwidth scale.

When the acre-counter is used for measuring the length
or width of a field, it is handled much as a draftsman han-
dles a divider in finding distances upon a map. In this
case, the device is given a half-circle swing, then another
half-circle swing, until the end of the field is reached. The
distances of field length and width are recorded in armstretches and decimal parts of an armstretch. To find the
number of acres, multiply together the length and width

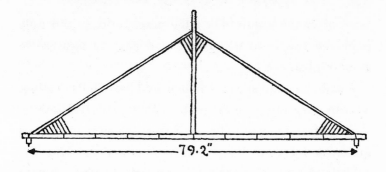

The acre-counter

and divide the result by 1000. The method is both simple and accurate.

In Retrospect

With the comments on present-day trends in measurement, the story of weights and measures comes to a close.

Reference was made on the first page to the measurement of the acre. It told how I, as a boy, had reached the conclusion that the acre and its measurement was something that a *boy* should not be supposed to understand. On a closing page of the story as I have set it down is described a device, based in idea upon the measuring system of early England, that makes the measurement of the acre easy to carry out and the acre itself easy to understand. A boy can operate the device. Looking back over the book's pages and thinking of my own school days, I wish that every country school of today had, in its museum, either an acre-counter or a replica of the knotted rope of chain length. Then the acre, furlong, and mile could be simple to understand and easy to measure in their original units.

I wish, too, that such a school would have in its museum various measuring rules, each with units divided in a decimal-fraction way. The trend in industry is away from common fractions toward decimal fractions, and the schools of America need real equipment to give constant practice in using decimal-fraction measurements. I feel that visits should be made to stores and shops that have self-registering scales or vending machines giving decimal-fraction readings. The older boys and girls should have the machinist explain the operation of his mike, the surveyor should be asked to tell of his instruments and how he measures distance along a line that goes down into a valley or up across hills.

A cash register and some form of calculating machine should be available to the boys and girls and their teacher. Most certainly, the solving of problems in arithmetic should not be looked upon as a matter of drudgery. The topic of measurement, in that subject, should be something vibrant and alive—a way of recording the outcome of the harvest, a way of determining the dimensions of a bridge for spanning a stream, a way of stating the size of a molecule or the distance to some fixed star.

Index

(Page numbers of illustrations are indicated by italics.)

acre, 25, 27, 93, 116, 117
Alexander the Great, 90
Alfred the Great, 18, 21, 30, 36, 105
Angles, 16–17, 20, 23, 27–29, 31–32, 39, 44–46
apet, 49, 70
armstretch: Egyptian, 48, 57, 68, 77, 85; English, 23–24, *24*, 25, 26, 31, 48, 77, 93, 116
Athens, 84, 88, 90
Augustus, 91

Babylon, 64–65, 67, 81, 82–83
barrel, 107–108
Beirut, 62
beka, 83, 87, 89
bema, 85, 86
Black Sea, 78, 84, 110
bowl-full, 33
Britain (Roman province), 13–16, 99–100
Bruges, 103, 109, 110
bushel: English, 130; "London," 129; United States, 129
Byblos, 62
Byzantium, *see* Constantinople

cable-length, 49
cent, 120
centimeter, 126
chain (chainlength), English, 23, 24, 25–26, 27, 116, 117; cf. Egyptian khet
Champagne, 110
Charlemagne, 23, *124*
chenica, 69
cloth-yard, 86
Cologne, 104, 109
Constantinople, 103, 110
cord, 40
Corinth, 84
Croesus, 76–77
cubit, 58
Cyprus, 63–64

daktylos, 90, 91
Damascus, 67, 101
Danes, 18–20, 22, 23, 39
decimeter, 123, 124
dime, 120
Dniester River, 78, 79
dollar, 120
dram (dram-weight), 87, 110, 131

Edward III, 21, 105
eighth-hundredweight, 41, 43
ell, 38, 39

farthing, 120
fathom: English, 23, 119; French, 122, 124; Greek, 86; Phoenician, 86; Roman, 94
fingerwidth: Athenian, 89, 90, 91; Egyptian, see zebo; English, 24, 25, 117; Greek, 90, 91
foot: English, 81, 98, 99; French, 124; German, 94, 104, 126; Roman, 93–94; Spanish, 93
forearm length, Athenian, 89
Franks, 94
furlong, 23, 24, 25, 26, 49, 93, 117; square, 26, 117

gallon: English, 130; United States, 130
Gebal, 62, 63, 65, 67, 68
Genoa, 103, 112
gerah, 69, 83
Goths, 79, 80, 93
grain: Babylonian, 83, 87; English, 130; Greek, 87, 110
grain-pint, 129, 130
gram, 123, 124
Gunter, Edmund, 114–18
Gunter's link, 117–18

half-fingerwidth, 31–32, 34
half-hundredweight, 41, 43, 105
half-mahi, 82, 87; see also mahi
handbreadth: English, 31–34, 123; Phoenician, see tefah
Hastings, Battle of, 96
Henry III, 97, 98

hlot, 33, 34
hundredweight, 41, 93

inch, 98, 104, 123

Jefferson, Thomas, 120
Johanssen, Carl M., 134
Jutes, 13, 16, 22

kernel-weight, 71, 83
khet, 49; royal, 61
Khufu (Cheops), 50, 61
kilo, 85
kilogram, 124
kilometer, 127
Knut (Canute), 100

Laplace, Pierre Simon de, 122
Lebanon mountains, 61–62
libra, 92, 105
lippy, 33
liter, 123, 126
litra-weight, 87
log, 69
London, 14, 16, 98–103, 107–109
Lübeck, 104, 109, 110, 120, 126

mahi, 58, 60, 85; royal, 59–60; see also half-mahi
maneh, 69, 75, 77, 83, 89
measure-full, 32, 34, 41, 69, 93, 123
measure-weight, 41, 123, 124
Memphis, 49–50, 61, 65
Menes, 50, 53–56, 55, 57–60
meter, 122–23, 124
mile, 118–19
Miletus, 88
mill, 120

Napoleon, 125
nent, 49, 68, 85, 86; royal, 60
Nile River, 48, 50–52
Nürnberg, 108

Odessa, 78
Odin, 78–80
ounce: avoirdupois, 103–106, 111; fine, 131; troy, 109, 111, 131
ounce-sterling, 109–110
onze, 109
onzia, 105

palm-width, Athenian, 89
peck, 33–34
pence, 120
penny, 120
Petrie, W. M. Flinders, 22–23, 24, 25, 27, 32, 47–49, 50, 58, 70, 97, 123, 128
Phoenicia, 62, 67–70, 77–78, 79–80, 82
pint: English ("London"), 107–108, 130; United States, 129, 130
pole, 38
pondus, 92, 107
pound, avoirdupois, 103–106, 111, 127, 129
pound-sterling, 109, 120
pous, 85, 86, 87, 90

Rhodes, 89
rod, 38–39, 39, 93, 97–98; king's, 97, 97–98
Rome, 90–93, 94

Saxons, 17–18, 22, 45, 100
score, 39

scruple: Babylonian, 83; Greek, 87, 110, 131
sea-mile: English, 119, 121; French, 122
shekel, 69, 75–76, 76, 82, 83, 89
Sidon, 67, 75
skaar, 39
skale, 42, 42–43
skale-weight, 41, 42, 69, 77, 83, 93, 105, 106
skeat, 41, 69, 77, 123–24
skore, 39
Solon, 87–90, 88
span (span-of-length): Egyptian, 57; English, 24, 25, 49, 117
stone (stone-weight), 41, 43, 105

tankard-full, 33, 34, 41, 69, 93
Tarshish, 68, 75
tefah, 68–69, 82, 83
thousand: Egyptian, 49; English, see thus-hund
thumb-breadth: Babylonian, 82, 83, 86, 87; English, 38–39, 98
thus-hund, 24, 25, 49, 119
ton: "London," 108; long, 106; metric, 124; short, 108
tonne, 124
Troyes (Troy), 108–111
tun, 33, 93
tun-weight, 41, 105, 124
twelfth-weight, 87, 111
Tyre, 67, 75

Ugarit, 65
unch, 98
uncia, 91–92

Venice, 103, 112

wand, 31, 31, 32, 38, 98, 123, 124

Westminster Abbey, 21, 97, 105

William the Conqueror, 96

yard, 98

zebo, 49, 60, 70–71, 83, 85–86, 89; royal, 60